CHILD OF THE TID
A Sea Trout Handbc

F. O'Reilly

CHILD OF THE TIDES

A Sea Trout Handbook

EDWARD FAHY

GLENDALE PRESS

First published in Ireland by
THE GLENDALE PRESS
18 Sharavogue
Glenageary Road Upper
Dun Laoghaire
Co. Dublin, Ireland

ISBN 0 907606 31 8

Cover design and painting
'Waterville sea trout'
by Richard Ward

ORIGINATION BY

PRINT PREP

DUBLIN

For Liz and Di and Tristan

Contents

Acknowledgements

Friends and colleagues have given invaluable assistance with the information contained in these pages. J J Nixon, Inspector of the Connemara and, later, the Ballinakill Fishery Districts, provided generous guidance and often gave practical help with the collection of material. He assembled the fishery registers on whose contents much of this work is based. Ruary Rudd of Waterville, Co Kerry, collaborated in the elucidation of a number of the topics discussed; he read through the manuscript and suggested many amendments to the text. John O'Connell, also of Waterville, and Eamon Cusack, Fishery Inspector of the Dublin District, supplied data, and made biological material available. Paddy O'Flaherty, who has since become Inspector of the Connemara District, participated in the investigation of sea trout producing catchments there. The Byrne family of Wicklow town introduced me to their fishery. To all of these and to my colleagues, Barney Doolin, Dick Fluskey and Nigel Bond, for their assistance on field work, I express my gratitude. The onerous chore of proof reading was undertaken by A.J. (Jack) O'Sullivan and Anne Marie Carruthers, to whom I am particularly grateful.

Some of the Figures which illustrate the work were drawn from material kindly supplied by the following: Dr Colm O'Riordan and his staff in the National Museum of Natural History, Dublin (Figs. 1, 39 and 40); Ruary Rudd (Figs. 41 and 42); Dr Andrew Ferguson (Fig. 47); Roy Eaton (Fig. 50); J.J. Nixon (Fig. 53); John Molloy and Dr R Bailey (Figs. 23 and 24). The following have been drawn from Figures contained in other texts, references to which are in the Bibliography: Figs. 23 and 24 — M.A.F.F. (1981); Fig. 26 — Barrett and Yonge (1958); Fig. 32 — Pemberton (1976); Fig. 34 — Dawes (1947); Fig. 46 — Varley (1967); Fig. 48 — Campbell (1979); Fig. 49 — MacCrimmon (1971), MacCrimmon and Campbell, (1969) and MacCrimmon and Marshall (1968).

Some of the text has already appeared in substantially similar form in the pages of *Salmon and Trout Magazine* and *Trout and Salmon*.

Foreword

Brown and sea trout are now regarded as one species, *Salmo trutta*, but that was not always so. In the latter half of the nineteenth century these two forms, and various other salmonids, were accorded separate species rank. In *Child of the Tides*, Edward Fahy examines factors which have a bearing on the inter-relationships of the constituent races and strains of sea trout. While considering these he deals exhaustively with many aspects of the behaviour and life history of the fish. The book is of particular interest to anglers as full recognition is given to the writings of the various angling authors who have considered sea trout.

One of the important technical findings described is the association of a genetic factor with certain kinds of trout. The factor has a high incidence in trout which have a long life expectancy and these include our most valuable stock of long-lived sea trout and the great lake trout, *Salmo ferox*. The life expectancy of trout is always of interest to anglers because the longer a fish lives the larger it can grow.

Among the numerous illustrations in *Child of the Tides* are maps showing where trout make vigorous growth (mainly in the Irish Sea) and the freshwaters in which long-lived sea trout spawn. Unfortunately, the only Irish catchment in which long-lived sea trout have been recorded to date is Waterville in Co. Kerry. This is a great pity because there is excellent sea trout fishing in the mountainous areas of Wales whose long lived sea trout avail of rich feeding in the Irish Sea. If the Avoca River in Co. Wicklow were not poisoned by the mines below Avoca, it and its tributaries, the Avonmore and Avonbeg, would equal the best Welsh rivers. The same could be said of the River Dargle at Bray, Co. Wicklow, if the trout there were not poached to such an appalling extent.

There are records of catches from well known sea trout fisheries, some dating from the mid-nineteenth century. One shows numbers and average catch weights of sea trout landed at the Inver fishery in Connemara between 1919 and 1974. I was particularly interested in this record as I had undertaken the improvement of that fishery in the mid 1940s, renovating the spawning beds and constructing additional ones and putting a size limit of twelve inches on any sea trout kept. The fishery at that time was privately owned and rods were not set to other anglers. Consequently the amount of fishing was reduced and the average weight of catch improved.

Edward Fahy has been working on salmon and sea trout for several years and he has published many papers on them. His book presents his findings to the angler and the naturalist. *Child of the Tides* is a most interesting and up to date natural history of this, possibly the most fascinating of our game fish.

Dick Harris, Rathgar, Dublin.

Introduction

If the biologist is the high priest of sea trout science, the angler is no less important a member of the Faith. It is the angler who, for more than a century, has put in the hours on the river bank, observing and protecting a fragile and ever more threatened resource. It is that hybrid of the two, the angling writer, who has done so much to publicise the fish and to interpret, from fragments of evidence, its place in the scheme of things.

For a fish of its size and economic importance the sea trout has received less than its share of scientific investigation and more than its quota of angler speculation. Sea trout have a special place in the heart of fishermen, being regarded as more fickle and moodier and, pound for pound, better fighters than salmon. When the fish in question is fast, beautiful and enigmatic, the most colourful of prose can be expected when the enthusiast describes it. Hamish Stuart probably expressed the love of the hunter for his quarry most colourfully in passages like:

> The fresh fish is joyous with the charge of life and feels the same gladness as when the sea was salt in his lips for the first time in his strange eventful history. He is bright and brisk, stout and strong. The stored strength of the sea quivers in every fin. His eye is that of the hunter, keen to note his prey. The questing habit is strong upon him; he is still a Nimrod, still as truly a nomad as when he roamed the estuary, coming and going with the green rush of the tides, hunting hard and feasting high, garrisoning his sides with oily sustenance.

Stuart had a healthy scepticism for scientists, 'the law should recognise the sea trout as a trout and should not identify the fish with the salmon.' His ideas provoked an appraisal of kelt sea trout by querying whether they should, like salmon, be afforded legal protection. Questioning assumptions can be a valuable service even if the conclusions drawn are not always correct. Stuart's ideas were controversial, even among his brother anglers. Henry Lamond wrote of him:

> ... I think it will serve all practical purposes if I advise the reader to adopt whatever implement or method Mr Stuart decries; to question the truth of all the principles he advocates and to deny his right to allege there are no convincing arguments in favour of methods other than his own ...

The angling lobby to which both men belonged has a most important part to play in the conservation and management of sea trout which, since the nineteenth century, have been regarded as at least as much a sporting as a commercial fish. It is a tradition established by the angling lobby rather than an idea promoted by scientists which extended protection to finnock (the smallest sea run trout) and thus provided a rudimentary conservation measure.

The earlier scientific workers like W.J.M. Menzies and G.H. Nall had strong angling connections; the fact that scientists and anglers have drifted apart since is symptomatic of our more specialised modern world. As early as 1927 R.A. Chrystal, an angler himself, had observed:

> Anglers are strange creatures and, even in this year of grace, one finds them holding strange theories as to trout, many of which have been exploded by scientists thirty or forty years ago.

The evolution of fishing methods and the changing expectations of anglers are a continuous process. The nature of scientific endeavour has also changed so that men like G.H. Nall, who painted a vast canvas, have been replaced by specialists, each shaping a small piece of a vast jigsaw.

The following pages endeavour to answer the questions most frequently posed by anglers and naturalists. The individual sea trout is examined and its external appearance is described. The significance of its livery, shape and of the marks and scars inflicted by unsuccessful predators, including man, is evaluated. An understanding of the life history is essential, and here it is given with an account of the associated terminology and the legal implications. Various kinds of sea trout stocks are described, together with the consequences of the biological facts for commercial and sporting fisheries. Angling statistics are scrutinised and advice is given on compiling and elucidating catch logs. A reconstruction of the history of sea trout fisheries is attempted. Factors which contribute to the making of big sea trout are investigated. A general preoccupation is the conservation and management of this form of trout and, in this context, the benefits and drawbacks of size limits and the use of hatcheries in the propagation of the fish are evaluated.

Sea run forms of the brown trout are now widely distributed around the world and, although much of the information presented here has been collected in western Ireland, it is relevant elsewhere. There is frequent cross reference to the phenomena described occurring in Britain. For completeness sea run forms of two North American species, brook trout and rainbows, are compared with European sea trout.

The aim of this handbook is to reconcile the many and often conflicting theories of scientist and angler. Neither has a complete understanding of sea trout but each has a valuable insight. It is hoped that these pages make some contribution to a continuing exchange of ideas.

1

A Trout in the Hand

Sea trout are a valuable catch but they exert a fascination for the angler which far exceeds their commercial worth. As a sporting fish sea trout are hard and spectacular fighters, and their enigmatic excursions in and out of fresh water have provoked much speculation about their biology. This handbook is an attempt to describe their variability of form and to appraise environmental influences on their life style. The objective is not to demythologise this beautiful and well-adapted fish but to provide a greater understanding and appreciation of its uniqueness. Today arguments are usually clinched by scientists, but some of the great intuitive interpretations of sea trout biology have come from the angling community, probably more so for sea trout than any other fish. Here an attempt is made to amalgamate the two approaches.

Brown trout, the species *Salmo trutta* to which the sea trout belongs, ranges naturally through Europe. Since the late nineteenth and early twentieth centuries it has been established by man in countries as far apart as Asia, Africa and the Americas. Consequently it co-exists with a number of other salmonid species. In common with these it has an adipose fin situated just in front of the tail and consisting of fatty tissue, without fin rays or spines. Although trout occur with a number of other salmonids the species with which it is most often confused is the Atlantic salmon, *S. salar*. The larger adult trout and salmon are sufficiently alike for salmon of inferior quality to be labelled and sold as 'sea trout', this obtaining usually a lower price on the market.

Salmon can be distinguished from brown trout of the same length by a number of characteristics: trout are stockier and this is particularly shown in the width of the caudal peduncle, or wrist, just before the tail. Picking up a large fish by gripping the body before the tail is often recommended as a way of distinguishing the two species. In salmon the wrist is sufficiently thin to enable a firm and confident grip; the larger trout may simply slip through one's grasp. The scales of sea trout are smaller than those of salmon and a simple microscopic examination may serve to disitinguish the two species. Macroscopically, there are fewer rows of scales (10 to 13) between the rear edge of the adipose fin and the lateral line in salmon than trout (13 to 16). The salmon tail is more deeply forked than that of the trout although this characteristic, as will be seen, is very variable.

Trout are altogether more aggressive in appearance, the upper jaw (maxilla) extending back behind the hind margin of the eye. In salmon the upper jaw reaches the posterior margin of the eye but no further. The roof of the mouth (vomer) in salmon has a staggered row of teeth while in trout they occur in a patch.

While these criteria are straightforward enough, both salmon and trout can be physically very alike and for almost a century Ireland's record trout was in fact a salmon. Known as Pepper's Ghost (Fig 1) it was caught on September 1, 1861 in Dooras Bay, Lough Derg (the Shannon system). It weighed 30.5 lb (13.8 kg) but turned out, on a more detailed scale examination, to be a salmon of four sea winters. Such fish were common in the Shannon system before the construction of Ireland's first hydro-electric scheme there.

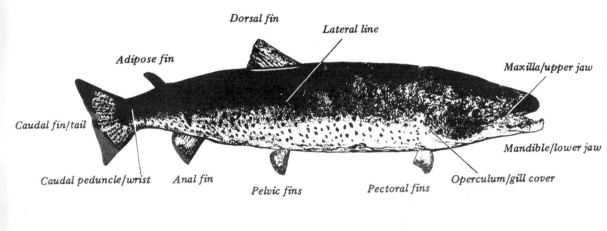

Dorsal fin

Lateral line

Adipose fin

Maxilla/upper jaw

Caudal fin/tail

Mandible/lower jaw

Caudal peduncle/wrist   Anal fin

Operculum/gill cover

Pelvic fins   Pectoral fins

6 in (15 cm)

Fig. 1   *Pepper's Ghost, dead and varnished, illustrating the external salmonid anatomy.*

Distinguishing salmon from trout is complicated by the existence of hybrids which arise from cross-fertilisation of the two. Once, these were regarded as something of a novelty and quite rare but more recent studies have revealed that they are fairly plentiful in nature; as many as 0.4 per cent of commercial catches were shown to be the progeny of inter-breeding in a British study published in 1972.

Physical dimensions then are not completely reliable as a method of telling salmon and trout apart and a microscopic scale examination is referred to in cases of doubt. This is not foolproof either and recently more exact chemical techniques have been devised to accomplish the task. The technique known as *electrophoresis* was developed in the

1960s to analyse the chemical composition of fish. Electrophoresis uses a technique of separating proteins which have a slightly different chemical composition (are polymorphic) and occur in variable form in a species. By examining several kinds of proteins and analysing their frequency a 'chemical fingerprint' is composed. Biochemical analyses of this kind provide decisive and certain identification of salmonid species and they go further. Using these techniques it is possible to explore below the species level, to sub-species, race and even to identify populations from individual rivers. Electrophoresis can be used to elucidate relationships among populations and to trace the evolution of salmonids and it is the means of confirming the existence of distinctive forms of trout and of ascertaining whether variation in physical form is a true reflection of a separate genetic strain.

But there are limits to electrophoresis. To date the techniques have not been developed to distinguish a sea-run from a freshwater brown trout and one must fall back on other criteria for a definition.

Trout, in common with all freshwater-based salmonids, are migratory. They move some distance, though it may be only a few metres, between spawning and feeding places. Some undertake longer journeys but the length of migration is a matter of degree rather than kind. Thus a 'freshwater' trout will descend from its spawning stream to the main river or lake where it feeds and grows before returning to that stream to breed. This pre-supposes there will be adequate feeding downstream in freshwater. Where the natal stream is within close range of the sea the trout will feed there instead.

It is reasonable to take the view that sea trout are a product of geography and environment rather than genetics and they should not be regarded as more than a form of brown trout. As for other salmonids, the introduction of 'resident' brown trout to salt water will not necessarily result in their demise.

The definition of sea trout is difficult and, before they have been to sea, impossible, although in time some genetic factor predisposing certain individuals to a saline environment will probably be discovered. In the meantime a river or lake system which produces sea trout qualifies as a sea trout system. And sea trout are simply trout which are caught in the sea or display signs of having been there. The latter is deduced when the trout show signs of rapid growth and the nearest available feeding area is the sea. The signs can be confirmed by reference to the scales.

A proposition, to which this author subscribes, states that the term 'sea trout' would be more accurately written 'salt water trout'. This would overcome the difficulty of stating just how far seawards a particular individual has migrated. Circumstantial evidence, such as a short absence period, suggests that a proportion of trout does not go beyond their estuary in a particular year although they might do so in the following one. Fish of this kind are termed 'slob trout'. Some scientists believe it feasible to recognise slob trout on their appearance and scale formation but this author is not confident about so doing.

Insufficient is known about the migratory habits of the majority of sea trout in any but a very few stocks which have been studied and the sedentary behaviour of supposedly more resident individuals would have to be compared with these. Both kinds go seawards and their physical features are too variable to be a reliable indication of how far. Systematically both should be grouped together and if 'sea trout' is not a reliable term, 'slob trout' is equally unacceptable. 'Salt water trout' could be a compromise, though perhaps a bit prosaic for the fish which Hamish Stuart affectionately and romantically described as 'a child of the tides'.

2

Form and Function

The three trout shown in Fig. 2 were captured using a fine meshed mono-filament net in a sea lough in Co. Donegal*: by definition, all are sea trout. If asked to comment on the catch an angler would certainly use the criteria, if not the seventeenth century terminology, of Izaac Walton to describe it:

> ... there be ... many kinds of fish and ... trouts especially; which differ in their bigness, and shape, and spots and colour.

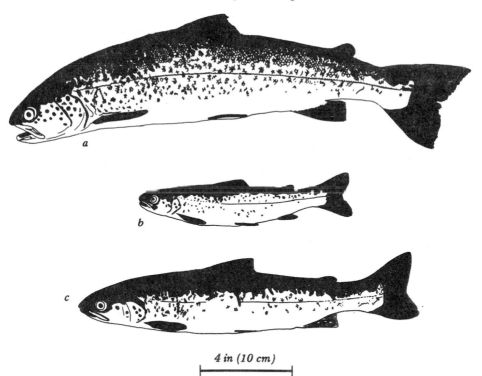

4 in (10 cm)

Fig. 2 Trout captured in a western sea lough in December: (a) trout in its third sea winter; (b) trout in its first sea winter (an autumn descending brownie); (c) trout in its second sea winter.

*The western sea lough referred to throughout is Mulroy Bay in Co. Donegal.

Every physical modification has a sound explanation in nature although it is not always easily recognised. For this reason scientists in the nineteenth certury catalogued a bewildering array of trout species; H.G. Seeley in 1886 listed twenty-nine. Their dilemma, of separating apparently distinctive physical forms, was complicated by the poorly understood life cycles of salmonid fish. Occasionally juveniles were attributed to a different species than their adults. The taxonomic problem was settled for a time by recognising just one species of European brown trout and laying less emphasis on its constituent populations while appreciating they could, even if seemingly different, interbreed to produce fertile offspring. In reality the opportunity to do so seldom arose because trout spawn in their natal streams and such specific behaviour promotes isolation in small populations which as a result evolve distinctive characteristics.

Having gone through a relatively simplified phase science can now return to a more mature appreciation of nineteenth century observations. The part played by different phases of the migratory life cycle is more fully understood and modern chemical techniques support the contention that real rather than apparent strains of trout occur.

To prepare a list of unique trout populations would probably be an impossible task. Investigations confirm that some kinds of physical variation can be the result of geographical or other types of reproductive isolation. Others arise from environmental influence, such as the abundance of sea feeding. For some of the observed biochemical characteristics there is as yet no known functional significance nor recognisable physical manifestation.

Sea-going trout share the physical attributes of neighbouring resident forms. But even within a single population there will be a change of shape as the trout grows. Most frequently commented upon by fishermen are the shapes of the head and tail, so an account of these is given. The curious angler will also examine the gut contents to ascertain how his quarry has been feeding, so the structure of the alimentary canal is described. The most obvious feature of all, sea trout coloration, will be considered first.

Colour: a seasonally changing livery

W.J.M. Menzies observed that, if called upon to select an 'average' sea trout he would envisage a fish of 2.5 lb (1.1 kg), straight from the sea at the end of June, blue rather than brown in colour, its spots black without any tinge of red. This image is widely established but there is another. R.A. Chrystal noted:

> We have the facts that both salmon and trout can be found in the sea in a highly discoloured state and freshwater trout of both brown and yellow appear perfectly happy there. In one of the South Uist lochs it is rare to kill a fish in September which is really completely

silvery, most of them are black, brown or yellow or a combination of these colours . . . they are trout of sorts of course . . . a transition stage between the freshwater and sea trout forms.

Menzies and Chrystal wrote mainly from Scottish experience but similar phenomena have been observed in Ireland. Dinneen's Irish Dictionary describes *Gabhlach* as '. . . closely resembling the white trout . . . in colour it is almost black above and of a dingy silver white underneath,' referring to a spring run sea trout in the autumn of its migration.

Two mechanisms contribute to the trout livery, background colour and spotting. Both are regulated through the agency of chromatophores, which are contained in cells occurring in the skin of the fish. Chromatophore-bearing cells are found in many classes of cold-blooded vertebrates and in shellfish (molluscs and crustacea). A chromatophore contains a quantity of pigment which, when it is dispersed throughout the cell, intensifies the colour in question; alternatively the pigment may simply be contracted in the chromatophore and so not very obvious.

In trout there are three types of chromatophore:

Lipophores contain the red and yellow carotenoids. These pigments also cause the 'pinking' of salmonid flesh and they are widespread in the animal world, occurring in creatures as diverse as shrimps and flamingoes (whose pink feathers are the result).

Melanophores harbour the brown, black and grey pigments and they are heavily concentrated on the back of the fish.

The other important substance contributing to pigmentation is guanin, an excretory product which occurs in the skin, scales and in the silvery layers of the eye. The *guanophores* which contain it expand and contract inversely with the lipo- and melanophores. Hence, the development of a sea-going silver livery suppresses the brown colours associated with residency in freshwater.

Regulation of the colour mechanism in trout is through hormones produced by the thyroid gland. Thyroid activity can be associated with the urge to migrate and the injection of thyroid extract precipitates a change from brown to blue-silver livery.

Coloration of a distinctive kind is a characteristic of certain recognised strains of trout. The gillaroo ('red fellow', a resident lake trout) which feeds on water snails is known for its red belly.

Spotting has also been invoked as a mechanism for recognising supposed strains of sea trout. The spots are aggregations of melanophores which assume x-shapes. For some strains of trout they would appear to have a diagnostic value but within sea trout catches from the same system there is a great deal of variability. G.H. Nall examined the intensity of spotting and its variation with age and sex on sea trout from Loch

Maree in Scotland, by the simple method of segregating samples of sea trout into categories of those having many or few spots. Among small fish in their first sea summer 50.5 per cent had many spots, while among large fish which first went to sea four years previously 54 per cent were heavily spotted. Few spots were recorded on 17.2 and 24.0 per cent respectively. An investigation of spotting according to sex revealed that 52.5 per cent of males and 56.7 per cent of females could be described as having many spots, 17.5 and 19.0 per cent having few.

The remarks of angling writers and scientists suggest that the brown and dark liveries are associated with autumn and the blue and bright sea-going coloration is a summer phenomenon. The general darkening of the fish as the year aged led some commentators to suggest that the number of spots increased as the season progressed. The proposition was tested by examining 250 sea trout captured in the Currane fishery* in Co. Kerry between July and early September 1980. The left side of the fish was visualised as consisting of four panels: the dorsal fin, the trunk above the lateral line, below the lateral line and the operculum (gill cover), and all spots on these were counted.

Spot number increased with the length of the fish but there was considerable variation in the numbers of spots on an individual of any size. In each week of the sampling period 20 trout of the same size were also examined, and throughout their average spotting intensity was fairly similar. Darkening of the skin in autumn then is caused by a dispersion of the melanophores and a consequent decline in the amount of guanin in the skin. Individual spots increase in size but not in number as a result. Spotting would seem to be a reliable, stable and hence good taxonomic characteristic of trout.

Coloration in animals is a protective measure which may serve to camouflage an individual or it may confuse or deter a predator. In trout obliterative shading obscures the fish against its background. A.C.L.G. Gunther considered a range of variations in trout coloration which

> ... with intense ocellated spots are generally found in clear rapid rivers and in small open Alpine pools; in the large lakes with pebbly bottom fish are bright silvery and ocellated spots are mixed with or replaced by x-shaped black spots; in pools or parts of lakes with muddy or peaty bottom the trout are of a darker colour generally, and when enclosed in caves or holes they may assume an almost uniform coloration ...

*The Currane fishery in Co. Kerry, south-west Ireland, is a part of the Cummeragh River system, a unique sea trout producer, to which frequent reference is made. The system contains the only documented long lived sea trout stock in Ireland. Lough Currane, the main fishing lake, adjoins the town of Waterville hence the fishery is known as Currane or Waterville.

Gunther's observations referred to resident freshwater trout but they are relevant to the freshwater phase of the sea-run fish. The purpose of blue livery in the sea will be equally obvious. From below, a trout belly would not stand out against the sky while from above its dark back would merge with the waves.

The distribution of the sexes between brown and blue liveries was recorded while examining brown and sea trout which were spawning in the Cummeragh river and lake system in Co. Kerry in the autumn of 1980. All occurred in the same spawning congregation, which is quite usual. Both of the sea-run trout in Fig. 3 displayed signs of sea-fed growth on their scales; the resident brown trout was a mature female of five winters.

The livery of the sea-run male was of the kind shown by the resident female. From the census of spawning fish 82 per cent of sea-run males but a mere 5.6 per cent of sea-run females could have been described as having the appearance of brown trout.

Thus the male sea-run trout in this instance either retained or reverted to the coloration associated with residence in freshwater. This observation prompts a number of speculations. In terms of biological expediency the female requires greater sustenance in order to manufacture eggs. Perhaps the female is better adapted to migrate to sea where food is more readily available? Certainly, as shall be seen, females often predominate among sea-run fish. Males, on the other hand, do not require so much food and indeed they may mature in freshwater before their first descent to the sea. In the Cummeragh census males were found in greatest numbers closest to the tide which would suggest they move shorter distances into freshwater than do females. All this implies that the majority of the so-called 'sloh trout' may in fact be males. That fact at least should be easy to ascertain.

The head: a means of sexing trout

The head of the spawning male salmonid is usually more powerful than the female's. The longer jaws of the male (or cock) fish are known as the *kype* (or beak). This may have a display function in reproduction, enabling him to keep others out of his territory. The head development consists of an elongation of the jaws and the growth of a terminal tooth-like process on the mandible (lower jaw). An extension and curving or hooking of the maxilla (upper jaw) completes the kype. In sea trout the growth of the kype does not necessarily coincide with sexual maturity. It is a gradual process which bears a closer relationship to the length of the fish.

An evaluation of kype development was made by expressing the

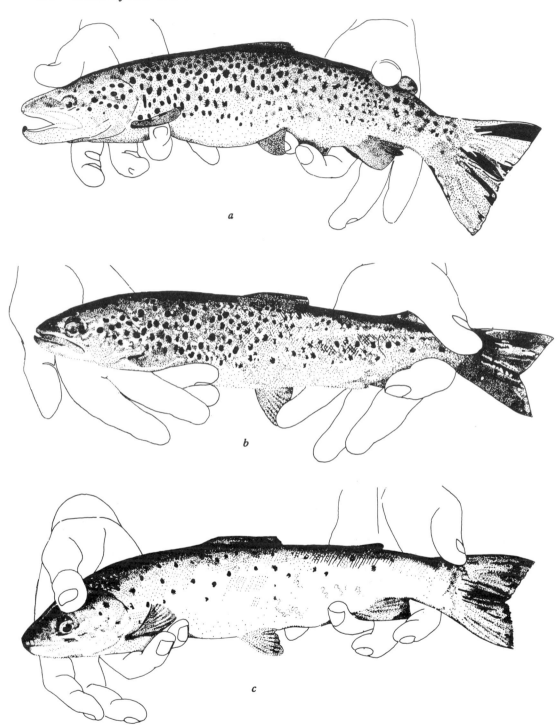

Fig. 3 *Livery of three spawning trout taken off the redds in the Cummeragh system in 1980: (a) male sea-run trout, (b) female resident brown trout, (c) female sea-run trout.*

length of the maxilla as a percentage of the fork length* of the fish. The development of the kype was traced by making measurements of a sample of 200 male and 200 female sea trout from the Currane fishery. Up to a fork length of 16 in (40 cm) the maxilla in the male (L. max in Fig. 4) was approximately 10 per cent of the fork length on average and this was

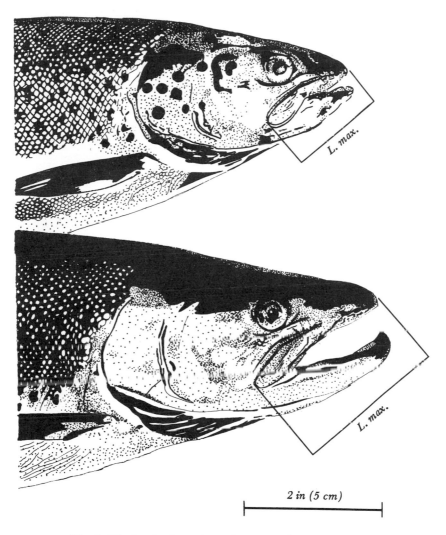

2 in (5 cm)

Fig. 4 The heads of two large i.e. greater than 20 in (50 cm) fork length sea trout, female above and male below. The length of the maxilla (L. max.) is used as an indicator of the development of the kype in the male.

Fork length is an important measurement which will recur in this account of sea trout. It is the length of the fish from the tip of the snout to the centre of the tail fork. The measurement should be taken on a fish measuring board.

slightly but not obviously longer than in the female. Above 20 inches (50 cm) fork length the kype rapidly develops and the sexes are easily distinguished by it. Below these dimensions the kype should not be relied upon and sexing should be undertaken by opening the body cavity.

Sexing trout on the redds is a more straightforward business than from material collected by anglers or netsmen during the summer months. Milt or eggs may be gently expressed from the body and even in males smaller than 16 in (40 cm) there may be a slight but noticeable kype development which is absent at other times of the year. The scales of males are more deeply embedded than those of females making them more difficult to dislodge. This is readily noticed when scale samples are being collected. The liveries of male and female trout are also often very different.

The tail of a trout: an unreliable diagnostic character

Although tail shape was in the past regarded as a key characteristic of certain kinds of trout, it was appreciated in the nineteenth century that shape altered as the fish grew. Francis Day in 1884 remarked of *Salmo nigripennis*, one of eleven trout species he listed:

> The caudal fin (tail) in the smallest has pointed lobes which become rouned in larger specimens.

The fuller tails of sea trout are still regarded as a reliable way of distinguishing them from salmon. Until quite recently the fullest tails were also thought to be a way of identifying what was regarded as a separate species of sea-run trout. Known as *bull trout* they were also called 'round tails' and according to W. Yarrell the tail of these fish assumed its square shape at an earlier stage than in salmon. Juvenile stages of the bull trout were never discovered but nobody was unduly concerned; so little was known of the life history of migratory salmonids that a link or two in the chain might pass its time unobserved, somewhere in the sea.

References to the bull trout occur frequently in the nineteenth and some twentieth century literature on sea trout. The River Tweed was thought to be a stronghold of the supposed species. There they were reported to attain a weight of 20 lb (9 kg) and bull trout of 15 lb (6.8 kg) were said to be frequent.

In 1928 G.H. Nall undertook an investigation of the bull trout of the River Tweed using an almost similar approach to that in his investigation of spotting on trout from Loch Maree. In all he examined more than 1,300 fish whose tail shape he classified as concave, square or round. At a fork length of 19.7 in (50 cm) the tail was square shaped in the majority of Tweed trout but at 27.6 in (70 cm) the posterior margin was distinctly rounded.

The alteration of tail shape is known to be an expression of growth.

Measurements taken of the centremost ray (the shortest in the tail) and the outermost (the longest) were made, together with a number of other physical measurements, of sea trout from Lough Currane in Co. Kerry and these indicate the way the tail shape alters. The centremost tail rays continue to grow as the fish extend at a faster rate than the outer fin rays. Thus the tails of all trout change from forked through concave and square to become convex in the largest specimens. Changes in shape are very slight and deciding which shape a particular tail belongs to can be difficult. An angler who is keen to ascertain the facts should examine his fish when it is freshly caught. Once the tail dries its margin becomes crinkled and the tiny distortions which result can be critical.

A fair amount of research has been carried out on the significance of tail shape to the life style of particular species. Tail shape corresponds with swimming speed. Fish with deeply forked caudals like the ocean-going tunny can make sustained swimming at high speed. Those with fuller tails, though capable of short, sudden bursts of speed, are comparatively slower swimmers. One account has credited the ocean-going sailfish which has a lunate (crescent-shaped) tail with a speed nearly three times as great as salmon and trout.

An explanation for the alteration of tail shape in salmonids as they grow could be their change of habitat from stream to sluggish river, lake or sea. A deeply-forked tail would be an obvious advantage to a young fish holding station against a fast flowing current. In the sea a fuller tail shape would provide the occasional burst of speed required to seize prey or to enable the fish to forge its way upstream to spawn.

As for the bull trout, there were several other characteristics by which they were identified. One of these was colour whose distinctive features did indeed change with a prolonged residence in freshwater. The only physical characteristic which did not was the tail shape. Menzies observed that in the space of 20 to 30 years the name was rapidly disappearing from the angling literature and Nall's work on the Tweed finally laid its ghost. He himself remarked: 'the fish are there but the name is dead.'

The trout gut: an efficient mechanism

Anglers frequently consult the stomach contents of their catch to obtain an augury of their prospects with a particular lure or fly. The naturalist can ascertain quite a lot about the recent history of a sea trout from the gut parasites it contains and, even if the fish is taken in freshwater, its earlier diet in the sea may be identified by examining the food remains in the hindmost part of the alimentary canal. Parasite fauna and sea-feeding will be examined later. The main features of the gut are described here.

The most primitive fish, of which the parasitic lamprey is an example, have a very simple tube-like gut in which functionally different regions are scarcely distinguishable. In the majority of the more complex Teleosts (the bony fish to which salmon and trout belong) the mouth, or food-catching part of the canal, is succeeded by a stomach in which food is accumulated. The duodenum or pyloric region which follows the stomach secretes digestive juices and the food which is broken down there is absorbed by the intestine. Within the Teleosts there are modifications to these parts in the Mugilidae (grey mullets) for instance the intestine is comparatively long to provide a larger assimilative area. These fish also have a very muscular stomach which can be described as a gizzard, to grind up the vegetable material on which they live. A less pronounced but nonetheless recognisable gizzard also occurs in the freshwater resident gillaroo trout which feeds on molluscs (water snails), whose shells are broken up by the muscular contractions of the gizzard.

In very simple terms the sea trout can be described as an eating machine. The mouth is equipped with teeth on the jaws, the vomer (roof of the mouth) and the tongue, to hold its prey. On either side of the mouth cavity are the gill arches carrying the gill filaments by which the fish breathes. But the gill arches (Fig. 5) have a dual function. They bear a number of spines, directed inwards, which are known as *gill rakers*. In some Teleosts such as the allis shad these can be as numerous as 80 to 130 per gill arch. As water comes in through the mouth and passes out under the gill cover, oxygenating the gill filaments in the process, small

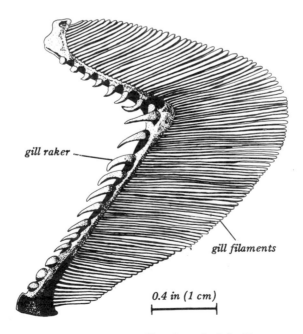

gill raker

gill filaments

0.4 in (1 cm)

*Fig. 5   The first gill arch on the left side
of a sea trout.*

planktonic organisms are sieved out of the current by the gill rakers. In sea trout the gill rakers could not perform such a fine task. Counts of their number on the first left side gill arch, of sea trout from the Lough Currane fishery in Co. Kerry, showed they could be as few as 14 or as many as 21; in 180 fish investigated they averaged 18. These figures are well within the limits of 13 to 22 given by L.S. Berg in his 1962 review of variations in the gill raker number of brown trout in the USSR and adjacent countries.

The stomach of sea trout can assume a number of forms or conditions which are thought to be dependent on circumstances. Salmonids are believed to engage in 'glut feeding' when in the presence of a plentiful food supply; glut feeding consists of gorging until the stomach is packed and it is followed by a relatively quiescent feeding period until the food has been digested. Cramming of food items is associated with a distended stomach wall. The organ assumes the appearance of a bag and all traces of the longitudinal muscle bands, at other times so obvious, are stretched out of the stomach wall. Or the stomach may be in a contracted state, its wall consisting of long muscle bands, its lumen (internal area) greatly reduced. Contracted and distended stomachs are reported from other fish such as cod but the significance of the conditions is not known with certainty. It is tempting to associate an enlarged stomach with active feeding and a contracted stomach with some kind of resting phase. However food remains are often found in contracted stomachs while the distended stomach is sometimes empty. While these facts do not discount an association of stomach condition with glut feeding, further information is required before conclusions are stated.

When the body cavity of a trout is opened the stomach lies alongside various other organs and extending the gut is a good way to examine it (Fig. 6). Behind the stomach the tract curves back alongside it and this part is known as the duodenum or pyloric region. The pyloric region is short and a large digestive area is required so its wall is extended outwards into a number of glove-finger like extensions known as *caeca*. If the pyloric region is dissected, its internal wall will be found to be similar to that of the pyloric caeca.

Taxonomists attempting to classify organisms take every opportunity to record countable features and pyloric caeca are an ideal example. Both they and gill raker numbers have been used with some effect to tell races and species of chars (the salmonid genus *Salvelinus*) apart and nineteenth century zoologists attempted similar exercises for *Salmo trutta*. Unfortunately many of their diagnoses were based on very few, occasionally even one or two, examples of the supposed species and like many countable and measurable characteristics of animal populations, numbers of pyloric caeca undergo some 'normal' variability, even within a population. Numbers of pyloric caeca could be a useful way of distinguishing races of trout and more information is certainly

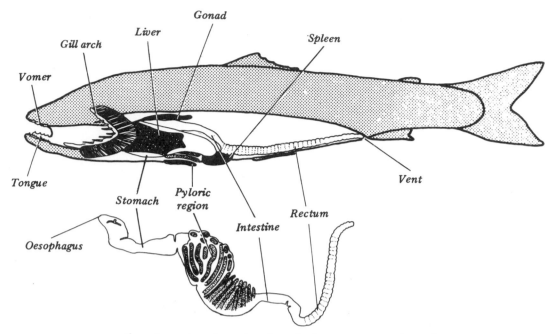

Fig. 6 (above) Section through a juvenile brown trout to show the disposition of the alimentary canal in the body cavity; (below) the alimentary canal extended to display the main organs.

Numbers of pyloric caeca in three collections of Irish sea trout

Percentage frequency distribution of fish in the three collections

Numbers of caeca	Irish Sea	Donegal	Lough Currane
Fewer than 35	4.8	1.0	1.9
36-40	25.3	11.5	13.9
41-45	32.5	33.5	39.9
46-50	18.1	24.0	26.4
51-55	9.6	21.9	12.5
56-60	8.4	6.3	5.3
61-65	1.2	1.0	—
More than 66	—	1.0	—
Number of trout in sample	121	195	208
Maximum number of caeca	61	66	60
Minimum ” ” ”	33	34	29
Average ” ” ”	43.6	47.2	44.5

required about them. The percentage frequency distributions of caeca in three collections of sea trout are given in the accompanying table to illustrate their range. There is so much variability in these numbers that it would be futile to base definitive statements on them. The averages though show some differences which could be meaningful. A smaller collection of 54 fish from the Lough Currane fishery, examined in another year, had a mean value of 44.7 per fish, almost identical with the average reported in the Table.

There has been a suggestion that caecal numbers in chars (*Salvelinus*) vary according to latitude, becoming more frequent as one proceeds northwards. The Donegal collection, which has the highest numbers recorded in the Table is the furthest north of the three discussed here. A similarly detailed account of pyloric caecal numbers in sea trout from Scotland, further north still, made in the 1920s is the only other available for comparison. Its average was 48.7 per fish, with a range of between 35 and 73.

Undoubtedly, as science progresses and finer discriminative biochemical techniques are developed, strains and races of sea trout will be identified. Caecal numbers will be useful corroborative proof of their existence but, on present information, they might simply be a result of environmental influence.

3

An Eventful Life History

Like salmon, trout are completely dependent on freshwater to reproduce. The eggs are laid in the autumn, in a redd (gravel excavated by the female). The following spring they hatch and, after a time, the juvenile is sufficiently large to migrate to its feeding and growing place. If it survives to maturity it will almost certainly return to spawn in the river system in which it was born, and very possibly to the specific tributary and even the same redd from which it emerged. Such are the essential details of the life cycles of Atlantic and Pacific salmon, char, brown and sea trout. But there are many ways in which trout can adapt to exploit their environment more thoroughly, in particular by modifying the nature and extent of the migration which intervenes between the juvenile and mature stages.

At one extreme small, 'stunted' brown trout in tiny streams and becks grow slowly, migrate only a few metres and produce very few eggs, as few as eight or nine, at maturity. The eggs are, however, large and a high proportion of them survives. The juveniles suffer only a light mortality and the end result is a lasting population. Small fish of this kind are only able to excavate shallow redds because they cannot generate the physical forces to dig deeper.

In an evolutionary context a trout which could excavate a deeper redd would establish its kind over a wider geographical area and thus benefit its species. Both sea and lake trout can do this, and their life strategies are quite different from those of stunted trout. They lay perhaps one hundred times as many eggs although each of them is smaller. The eggs are buried deeper in the gravel although their mortality is higher. In spite of this reduction in numbers the juveniles which emerge are sufficiently numerous to necessitate further thinning out by starvation.

Plasticity of form or life style in trout therefore represents a capacity to exploit a range of habitats and this is the reason for the species being so successful in competitive terms and so geographically widespread. For some of its life strategies the brown trout assumes the same shape and colour from early juvenile life to its death but the more adventurous its life style the more physically and physiologically demanding it becomes. The life of sea trout consists of a series of recognisably distinctive phases. Some of these like the smolt and the kelt the fisherman is legally required to know.

While the life cycle of the sea trout is essentially similar to that of the Atlantic salmon far more terminology is associated with it for several reasons: first, the sea trout does not migrate as far afield as the salmon; in fact its marine life is on the whole an inshore one so various stages of it are frequently encountered in the sea. Secondly, when salmon return to freshwater they do so to spawn and that is not necessarily true of sea trout. And finally, the sea trout is technically known as a multiple spawner, meaning that it can reproduce several times. Fish which have spawned seven and eight times have been reported. Few salmon, however, will spawn more than once and fish which have spawned three times are rare.

There is some debate about the terminology relating to the sea trout life cycle and in their straightforward approach fishermen may be more accurate than scientists, particularly where the term 'smolt' is concerned.

The egg

Compared with the eggs of cyprinids (coarse fish) the salmonid egg is very large. It also hatches earlier in the year. In the early spring there are fewer suitable organisms to serve as salmonid food and so, to tide it over, the young salmonid is equipped with a yolk sac (Fig. 7).

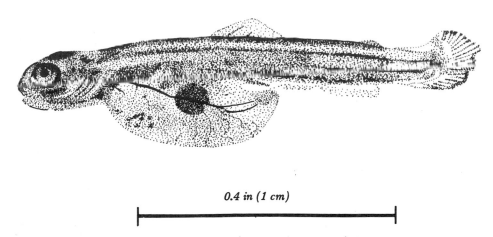

0.4 in (1 cm)

Fig. 7 A trout alevin or tadpole stage showing the yolk sac under the body.

The alevin

The first recognisable stage of the salmonid is known as the alevin or tadpole stage because of its resemblance to the young stages of the frog. As the newly hatched salmonid grows the yolk sac is absorbed and reduces in size. The fish emerges from the gravel in which the egg was laid and, before the yolk sac has completely disappeared, it begins to feed on tiny insects and crustaceans.

Fry and parr

The quest for food takes it out of but not far from the redd and when this movement has occurred, the relatively streamlined little salmonid is known as a fry. Once disperal from the redd has taken place the fish is known as a parr. By that time it should have developed the dark *parr marks* on its sides.

 The parr of Atlantic salmon co-exist with trout so a comparison of the two is apposite (Fig. 8). Even at this young stage when the fish may be only 1.25 in (3 cm) in length, the features which will later be of diagnostic value in separating their adults are apparent. The trout has a heavier build, in keeping with its preference for deeper, more sluggish waters than salmon. Its mouth is larger than that of salmon and the maxilla (upper jaw) extends to behind the eye in trout, to the centre of the eye in salmon. The caudal peduncle (the 'wrist' before the tail) is thicker in trout and the salmon has a generally more streamlined shape in keeping with its preference for the faster waters of stream riffles. Holding station against the current necessitates larger pectoral fins and those of salmon are more powerful than the trout's; the salmon tail is more deeply forked, an asset where stronger swimming is required and the darker parr marks of salmon are a useful camouflage in broken, fast flowing water. The trout has more orange spots on its body and the adipose fin is a brighter orange colour than in juvenile salmon.

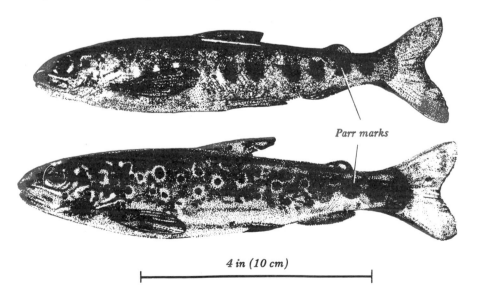

Parr marks

4 in (10 cm)

Fig. 8 Parr of salmon (above) and trout (below).

The smolt

Fishermen can readily recognise the smolt as the silvered transitional stage which takes the juvenile salmonid from freshwater to the sea. But trout can enter the sea at two times of the year and in two liveries. In the spring they are silvered and obviously smolt-like. In the autumn they are simply small brown trout whose numbers may exceed those of the spring exodus. The scientist working on the angler's or the netsman's catch will recognise the smolt from the scales as the transition between freshwater and marine growth irrespective of the appearance of the fish which actually made the journey downstream. Thus, to the fisherman the term smolt has a real meaning and he can associate the fish by its appearance with the term. The scientist cannot; he must depend on the kind of scale formation revealed by a fish which has returned from the sea. Indeed some American scientists have gone a step further in applying the term smolt to a rainbow trout which has descended from a nursery stream to a freshwater lake system. Although these rainbow trout do not silver, they do adopt a more streamlined appearance prior to descent, apparently anticipating a different way of life downstream.

Returning to sea trout, there are several kinds of true, spring descending smolts. *A-types* are bigger fish which attain migratory dimensions at the end of the previous year's freshwater growth. *B-types* must make up some additional length in the spring of their first descent to salt water. For these there is some additional freshwater growth, made in their year of first migration, shown on the scales. The nature and significance of A and B-type smolts are not fully appreciated and there will be further reference to them. Their definition depends very largely on scale reading but in many respects this has limitations — for example it is still not possible to tell autumn descending brown trout and spring descending A-type smolts apart on scale formation.

These reservations aside, it must be owned that the smolt dimensions deduced from examination of scale collections of sea trout have revealed consistent features of sea trout from the same river system, although they have been made over a period of years and by different investigators. The average 'smolt length' appears to be fairly constant in a particular river system, indicating the unique genetic constitution of trout there. The majority are two year old smolts (it is important to define the age of first descent to sea because the length at which it takes place is related to this, older smolts being larger than younger ones). In Ireland two year old smolts are generally in the vicinity of 6.3 to 8.7 in (16 to 22 cm) fork length. In the Currane fishery in Co. Kerry however they are consistently larger; comparable investigations in 1944 gave an average of 9.7 in (24.6 cm) and in 1980, 9.3 in (23.6 cm). This fishery is unique in a number of important respects in Ireland. It has equivalents in Scotland and Wales however, so that references to Currane have a wider application.

In shape the smolts of both salmon and trout are similar to the parr. In stocks whose smolt dimensions are small the smaller individuals can be well Conditioned* but a small proportion of these smolts achieve a greater than average length and these are very slim (Fig. 9). The smolt thus illustrates an important principle in sea trout growth: an extension in length precedes an increase in weight. In the case of these large smolts the weight gain comes later, in the sea.

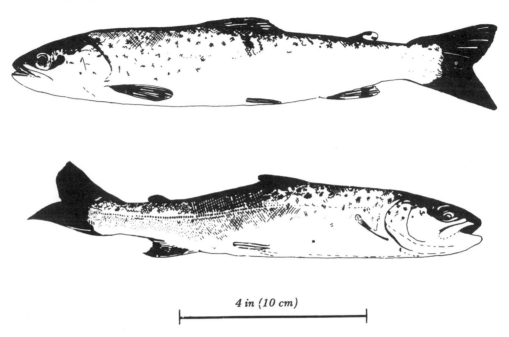

4 in (10 cm)

Fig. 9   Two aspects of a large sea trout smolt from the Screebe fishery, Connemara, showing its poor Condition.

Post-smolts

This phase commences once descending trout have reached the sea. It persists until after the first post-migration winter when the fish become 'adult' or 'sea trout'. Experienced handlers of sea trout can distinguish post-smolts by their silver-white coloration, their rough feel and readily dislodged scales. Post-smolt is a technical term. The fisherman will be more familiar with finnock, herling, whitling, harvest trout, harvesters, school peal, autumn trout and juners (or juniors). In some fisheries these make up the majority of the catch.

The transitional or smolt stage taking a parr to the sea is usually visualised as a silvered fish but it may be brown or partially silvered. In

Condition, referring to the fatness or shape of a sea trout, is written with an initial capital in this book.

the early months the post-smolt has yellow pectoral fins which lose their prominent colour as the fish grow. Menzies reported that in the Solway district the change in colour was incorrectly used by local fishermen to tell trout and salmon apart. Other mysteries are associated with the post-smolt, particularly its relevance in the sea trout life history. A conversation between anglers, retold by H.P. Henzell describes the dilemma:

Having landed a post-smolt:

'Put him back,' I told Hector, 'and maybe I'll hook him again when he is a better size, although I hear that the experts are saying now that the finnock isn't a sea trout at all but a separate species.'

Hector looked contemptuous. 'Aye,' he said. 'So I've heard; but if the finnock is not a young sea trout will you tell me what a young sea trout looks like?!'

Many scientific commentators have referred to the problem of evaluating, in the context of the sea trout life history and from the point of view of fishery yield, the post-smolt stage. If, for instance, post-smolts die without reproducing (and only a small proportion of them is known to reproduce) then this phase might be regarded as expendable and exploitable. Angling tradition has dictated otherwise and the tendency has been to conserve these fish.

Post-smolts are said to be equivalent to the *grilse* of Atlantic salmon. These fish mature after one winter at sea. (*Salmon* are *Salmo salar* of more than one sea winter at their first return to fresh water). R.A. Chrystal described this view which to the angler expresses an impression formed by the behaviour and appearance of the fish:

Now, to my mind, the whitling stage of the sea trout is an exact parallel to the grilse stage of the salmon, and here we have again the same distinctive features of immaturity, by which anglers distinguish them from the adult fish. But these whitling are not ascending their rivers to spawn although a few of them do so. The whitling however are bound by no fixed rules and may, and often do, visit freshwater several times during the summer and autumn after first descent, and may repeat this in the spring and the summer following. It is the habit of some people to give them the name of sea trout in this following season but personally, I always consider them as what I call 'second year whitling' since the grilse like characteristics are still noticeable. The forked tail is not yet squared-off, they present a juvenile outline, even though they may have in some districts, but not in all, attained a weight of two pounds or more.

In a scientific sense the foregoing is misleading. Grilse have, like all returning *S. salar*, completed sea growth prior to spawning. The purpose of their re-entry to freshwater is to spawn.

In the sea post-smolt sea trout may travel long distances from their natal river systems, or they may make a first return within two months. The first return may or may not be to the parent river and overwintering may take place in fresh water or at sea.

Some confusion in the definition of post-smolt occurs with autumn descending brown trout which silver-up in the sea. These were observed during the silvering-up process in sea loughs in western Ireland and some later migrants were still very small the following spring when, strictly, they should have become 'sea trout'. Tagging of these juvenile trout has revealed that some run into freshwater the following year, their scales similar to those of post-smolts.

Adult trout

Adult trout are all sea trout which have reached their first post-migration winter. This group comprises a number of others which may be referred to as *pre-spawned* (unspawned, maiden or virgin) trout which have not yet spawned and *previous spawners* which have done so. Some male sea trout probably first spawned as parr but traces of this are not detectable on the scales. Previous spawners can be described as *spents* (slats or kelts) if they are in poor Condition and have not recommenced feeding afterwards. In contrast, *clean* fish have either not spawned or have recovered Condition after spawning.

In the majority of fisheries the two age categories of greatest value to anglers are the post-smolt and the adult trout of one sea winter. As tradition has widely extended protection to the younger age group (particularly in Scotland), one sea winter fish have a particular value to the angler. Hugh Falkus recognised the older age group with confidence:

> It is important to remember that I refer specifically to sea trout with a sea life of one year and not to the young fish . . . a certain number of which continue to feed in freshwater as avidly as the food supply permits.

Falkus expressed the opinion that in their feeding habits post-smolts are a transitory stage between the resident freshwater form of brown trout and the sea-run adult fish which he states pertains more to the fasting salmon in its behaviour. Sea trout of one sea winter are larger than post-smolts and, because they have not commenced spawning in any great number, the majority are of relatively high Condition (i.e they are fairly plump).

The kelt

Izaac Walton's advice was straightforward:

> And next you are to note that till the sun gets to such a height as
> to warm the earth and the water, the Trout is sick, and lean, and
> lousy, and unwholesome; for you shall, in winter, find him to have
> a big head, and then to be lank and thin and lean . . .

But the sea trout kelt is not so readily characterised; men of good inten-
tions have very likely experienced a twinge of conscience or at least
doubt after landing a slim-bodied sea trout in the early months or indeed
at other times of the year. Henry Lamond, commenting on a catch
reported from Loch Lomond, observed that it probably consisted largely
of kelts which are to be looked for in the Leven in April and May. He
remarked:

> This does not call in question the sportsmanship of Franck (the
> 17th century author who described the fish) and his friends because
> kelts were lawful prize then but it certainly takes something from
> the presumptive value of the basket . . .

There is a real chance of confusing kelts with the incoming spring run of
large sea trout. However kelts may lie up in lakes into the summer,
particularly in a cold year and the fish drawn in Fig. 10 was taken by an
angler in July 1982 in Lough Currane. That it was a kelt was confirmed
by internal examination of the ovary and of the scales.

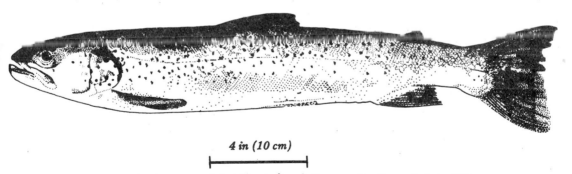

4 in (10 cm)

Fig. 10   A sea trout kelt taken in Lough Currane, Co. Kerry, in July 1982.

When Hamish Stuart disputed the definition of kelt sea trout he
expressed a very real frustration with and scepticism about the validity
of the term. His challenging the evidence was important in provoking
an appraisal of this phase of the life cycle. Logically Stuart's argument
was good, though based on false premises. First of all he believed that
sea trout feed in freshwater with the same avidity as resident brown
trout:

To treat kelt sea trout, i.e. a sea trout that has spawned but has not visited the sea or estuary after spawning, as similar to kelt salmon, is to ignore the fact that sea trout feed in freshwater and to overlook the effect of this habit . . . There are, in fact, only kelt sea trout in the same sense as there are kelt trout; that is to say, trout which have not recovered condition and are still lank and lean partly from the effects of spawning, but chiefly because their feeding and their food supply have been limited during the winter. Just as a trout recovers condition by feeding, so a sea trout kelt may become a well-conditioned fish, alike from the sporting and the edible point of view, without actually returning to the sea.

The consequence of Stuart's reasoning:

. . . we must treat the sea trout as the same in this respect as the brown trout, and hence we are entitled to hold that a kelt sea trout may be a kelt only because it has not returned to the sea and may therefore be in all respects, alike from the edible, the angling and every other point of view, as clean and as wholesome a fish, though perhaps not in such perfect condition as a sea trout that has been in the sea and the estuary from a considerable period.

In Britain and Ireland sea trout have traditionally been regarded as salmon in the legal sense and offering protection to the kelt was a consequence of this. Associating sea trout and salmon in the legal sense was denounced by Stuart:

It should be abundantly obvious that to read the two as the same — as our positive law, thanks to the ignorance and indifference of our legislators, invariably does, is to perpetuate an error . . . (and) fosters those traditional beliefs as to the life history and habits of the sea trout which have been the direct cause of all the confusion . . . it is necessary to add that the kelt sea trout . . . does not call for the same degree of protection as the kelt salmon.

If the last statement went a bit too far Stuart had sought a way around a very real problem. Menzies described it in the following terms:

A practical point which sometimes baffles anglers and even those who have the opportunity of wider experience is not how to define a kelt but how to detect it when landed. Usually, of course, it is obviously thinner than a clean fish. It is not so thin, however, as most salmon kelts, in which the middle section of the fish has the dorsal and ventral contours almost, if not quite, parallel. The fins may be frayed and for some time after spawning the vent is very much enlarged. The whole fish is soft, and after death . . . the flanks fall in and the flesh is very much paler than that of a clean trout of corresponding size.

Menzies went on to discuss the kelt which is gorged with recently consumed food, a habit he claimed was rarely indulged in by clean trout. In this case it may be necessary to empty the stomach *via* the mouth by gentle pressure before the shape of the body can be ascertained. He also considered the various degrees of spent appearance which result from a spawning migration of long or short duration. Once feeding recommences the bright external livery is quickly resumed and with it an appearance of recovery of Condition (i.e. fatness). In fact, Menzies reported, there is no real improvement in Condition until the fish go to sea and recommence feeding in earnest. Until that happens weight continues to be lost.

In fact it is doubtful whether kelt sea trout ever fully recover Condition. Fig. 11 shows two sea trout captured in the Irish Sea in May 1983. Their difference in Condition is obvious and their state of maturation was confirmed by post-mortem examination. The better Conditioned fish was pre-spawned, the other had spawned the previous winter. Both were gorged with food and both were, in theory, ready to re-enter freshwater.

The Condition of sea trout in Irish waters can be related to their diet. Where the trout prey largely or exclusively on fish their Condition is

8 in (20 cm)

Fig. 11 Two sea trout captured in the Irish Sea in May 1983: (a) well-Conditioned, pre-spawned; (b) poorly Conditioned, spawned the previous winter.

high; when invertebrates, like crustacea and insects, comprise the main food, Condition is low. However in either case Condition is highest among the younger sea age groups. Once spawning commences the older fish tend to conform to a similar weight at length relationship irrespective of their food, although at this stage the food of both groups consists largely of fish; presumably the larger trout of the stocks which subsist largely on invertebrates are sufficiently mobile to seek out fish prey.

In view of the foregoing, particular care should be taken with the term 'well-mended' kelt which should indicate brightness rather than Condition. Menzies concluded that the definition of a kelt sounded delightfully easy but its application was not so simple. The question of when estuary feeding sea trout cease to be kelts and again become clean fish almost defies solution and the problem is further complicated by the return to freshwater of sea trout which have made little sea growth and have a kelt like appearance. Without a scale examination and an investigation of the ovary it is difficult to reach a decision on kelt sea trout, although the presence of sea lice which have a marine origin discounts the possibility of the fish not having been back to sea.

Spring-run trout

One additional term to be explained is *spring trout*. These fish are regarded as exactly analogous to *spring salmon*. They move into freshwater, with the ultimate objective of spawning, in the months of March to May. Most are large and relatively old and their early ingress from salt water is a result of their completing feeding early in the year. Intermixed with the true spring run are adult trout which came into fresh water the previous autumn and possibly overwintered there without spawning, post-smolt and descending kelt sea trout.

All sea trout fisheries have some manifestation of a spring run but in most it is rudimentary. Spring running trout occur in greatest numbers in long lived stocks of which there is only one in Ireland, the Currane fishery in Co. Kerry; a further dozen or so are documented from Scotland and Wales.

4

Art and Science and Scale-Reading

Angling is an obsessive sport, a pursuit which involves reading and writing as well as physical activity; and yet, for all the details of catches lovingly recorded in fishing diaries, few anglers attempt to age their fish. Scale-reading is a technique used by scientists who can be, if not secretive, protective of their methods. Some have been known to describe scale interpretation as an art rather than a science, which is another way of saying one cannot always be very precise about it. Critical evaluation of the methods involved has been undertaken for sea trout. By tagging (marking) and later recapturing individuals whose age is therefore precisely known, a comparison of the known with the interpreted life histories is feasible. In these trials approximately 90 per cent of scales were correctly read.

Scale-reading is therefore not an exact science and that fact possibly discourages the angler from attempting it. Hamish Stuart whose notes date from the early 1900s, was a sea trout angler who was sceptical about its utility:

> The scale school profess to be able to tell the age, period of sea sojourn, whether a fish has or has not spawned, and so forth, merely from a study of a few of the scales on that fish. I venture to assert that most of their conclusions on the above points are inaccurate.

Scepticism is healthy and, as we shall see, scientists must double check their assumptions by reference to living fish as often as they can especially where such a subjective procedure is concerned. Much corroborative work on the interpretation of sea trout scales still needs to be undertaken by scientists but the basic methodology is well enough understood for others besides the specialist to make use of it with some confidence.

Sooner or later every fisherman is confronted by a salmonid whose identity is uncertain. Scrutinising the scales might decide the question; it would discrimate between salmon and trout and between sea-run and brown trout although it should not be used to differentiate 'trout' species (rainbows, browns and brookies). Or a fisherman might refer to the scales simply to find out something more of the life history of the fish he has caught.

Elaborate equipment is not required to ascertain details of the life of a trout from its scales. These are scraped from the 'shoulder' of the fish, just under the front end of the dorsal fin. They should be washed and placed, in a drop of water, on a piece of glass. There they may be read using a low power microscope or a hand lens. A magnification of ×20 should be adequate to identify the main events which have taken place in the fish's life, although such an arrangement will not serve to work on the finer details of scale structure or to make measurements to enable back-calculation of length at age. If scale-reading is attempted do not be satisfied with a single scale but instead consult at least three from the same fish; scales, like other details of the anatomy, are likely to vary in form.

Electrophoresis has been described as a means of obtaining a 'chemical fingerprint' of a fish but the analogy between fingerprinting and scale analysis will appear even more compelling. Fingerprints and scale structures look very similar consisting of a series of concentric whorls and rings from a central point to the perimeter. If this structure is not complete, if for example the centre does not have a ring structure, then it is very likely that the fish at some stage in its life history lost the scale which later regrew. These are called *replacement scales* and they cannot be interpreted.

The process of scale growth and development is considered in some detail here because it is a useful extension to the previous chapter and it gives an insight to the reasoning behind the legal distinction between brown and sea trout, the latter being regarded in British and Irish legislation as salmon. Before going further it would be as well to give a brief account of the shorthand adopted by scientists to describe the migratory salmonid life cycle.

The age of individual fish can be expressed by the convention:

$$x.y$$

where the freshwater (parr) life is described in years by x and y is the number of sea years, or more accurately, winters. Additional information is contained in the formula:

$$x.y + z \text{ S.M.+}$$

where z is the number of times a fish spawned (S.M. = spawning mark). A final plus sign signifies additional growth which however does not amount to a complete season's. A sea trout with the scale formula 2.1 + 3 S.M.+, spent two parr years in fresh water and four subsequent sea winters in each of the last three of which it spawned. The total age of the fish is 6+ years.

To appreciate how these events may be recognised from the sea trout scale it is necessary to understand the way in which scale growth occurs.

Scale formation

In all vertebrates the skin is composed of two layers. The outer (epidermis) in fish contains the chromatophores which decide its colour. The inner (dermis) is occupied by the *dermal skeleton* of scales. In Teleost (bony) fish these are thin, flexible and transparent. The simplest form is termed cycloid and trout and salmon, being primitive fish in an evolutionary sense, possess these. They are recognisable by their surface sculpture which consists of a series of concentric rings. Each scale is a platelet comprising two layers: a bony outer and a deeper fibrous lamellar layer.

As the platelet, composed of its two layers, grows, it tilts from its originally horizontal position to an oblique one. The anterior end of the scale sinks into the skin which forms a *scale pocket*, and the posterior end tilts outward. Most of the scale remains embedded in the scale pocket and the arrangement of the scales from front to back on the fish is like the arrangement of tiles, top to bottom, on the roof of a house.

Growth of the scale continues throughout the life time of the fish by addition to (accretion at) the margin of the bony layer. This layer is an organic framework impregnated with inorganic salts, mainly calcium phosphate and calcium carbonate.

The sculptural ridges or rings on the scale are called the *circuli*. They form when the quantity of bone-making materials exceeds what can be absorbed onto the growing edge. Hence circuli are generally thicker and more widely spaced in summer than in the colder months of the year. Their function is to anchor the scale to the skin.

Much of the intuitive interpretation of scale growth is made on a subjective assessment of circulus formation. Thicker and more widely-spaced circuli are associated with rich feeding conditions and vigorous growth and the contrast between sparse freshwater feeding and a more plentiful food supply elsewhere is indicative of a move from fresh to salt water having taken place. The best example of this is to be found in the scales of salmon (Fig. 12).* The scale which is reproduced belonged to a grilse. The contrast between the tight and narrow freshwater circuli (the parr phase occupying the very centre of the scale) and the explosive marine growth represented by thick and widely spaced circuli is typical of this species. It is quite different from scale formation in sea trout.

In fairly constant conditions of food supply and temperature circuli tend to form at an even rate so that their number is roughly proportional to the fork length of the fish. Within a population however, because the

---

*The drawings of salmonid scales which illustrate this chapter are labelled in accordance with the following convention: arabic numerals (1, 2 etc.) are used to indicate the end of a year's freshwater growth; Roman numerals (I, II etc.) the end of a marine year's. Spawning marks are labelled 1 S.M., 2 S.M. etc. Other phases of growth are identified as indicated in the captions.

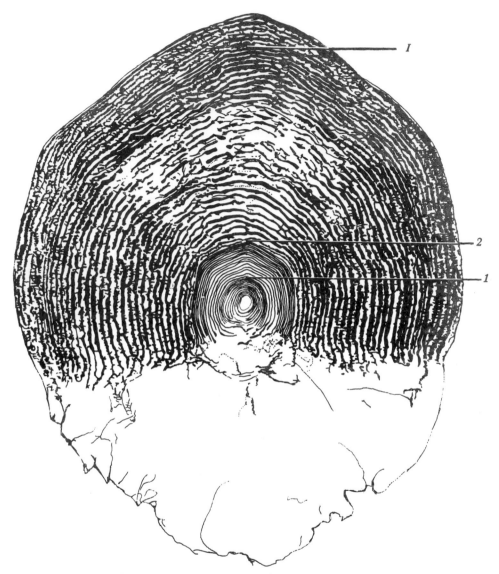

Fig. 12 Scale of a grilse (Atlantic salmon) with the formula 2.1+ (i.e. two freshwater (1,2) and one marine (I) winters). The fish weighed 8 lb (3.6 kg).

relationship is not very exact, circulus number is not a precise indication of the size of the fish. Scale dimensions are generally proportional to the fork length of a fish and this fact enables a back-calculation from its actual fork length to its length at an earlier stage in the life history, identified from the scale sculpture. Specifying how these phases are recognised is our next task.

Basically three features of scale sculpture are used to decipher the life cycle.

Checks

A check on a scale represents a slowing down or temporary cessation of growth which is later resumed. The typical pattern, indicating a season's growth, begins with relatively strong and widely-spaced circuli; in time these become thinner and separated by progressively narrower intervals. Observations on fish held in captivity have shown that better feeding and more suitable growing conditions favour the formation of strong and widely-spaced circuli and that a deterioration of circumstances, such as falling temperature, causes the thinner and more closely-spaced circuli to develop.

At a nigh magnification each circulus is discernible but at a lower power the thin circuli become blurred and are visible as an *annulus* or winter band.

The scale of the sea trout shown in Fig. 13 possesses several of the features already referred to. The progression from widely-spaced to narrowly-spaced circuli is apparent in both freshwater and marine years and the contrast between freshwater (the parr centre) and marine growth is also fairly clear. Comparison between this trout and salmon (Fig. 12) reveals how distinctive are their patterns of scale formation.

In the wild as opposed to artificial culture, the abundance of food and optimal growing temperatures are usually a feature of the seasons. This is not an invariable rule however and occasionally field observations support other explanations. The high temperatures of summer for example can inhibit growth and precipitate the slowing down of development and the formation of 'false checks'.

The equation of apparent annual growth with a definite calendar period should be confirmed by field observation. Nall and Menzies observed of trout in the Beauly Firth, that while some are passing through a resting stage in the rivers, a large number may be feeding freely on sprats and small herring. At the same time as the fish in freshwater have ceased to feed, the active feeders are found to be gorged and growing rapidly, laying down broad, widely-spaced circuli on the scales, so that winter growth takes the form of that usually made in summer. Conversely, as the spring advances and food diminishes in quantity, the winter feeders, along with the others which have spent the winter (or most of it) resting and fasting in freshwater, gradually move down the inner Firth and out into the waters in which the winter feeders evidently meet less favourable conditions, or reach a stage of repletion or fullness where less intensive feeding is a physiological necessity. A band of comparatively close ridges, which simulates in appearance a genuine winter band, is normally laid down on the scales at some period in the spring or summer. Nall and Menzies claimed:

> (there are) definite indications that heavy feeding and rapid growth during the winter is frequently, perhaps normally, followed by

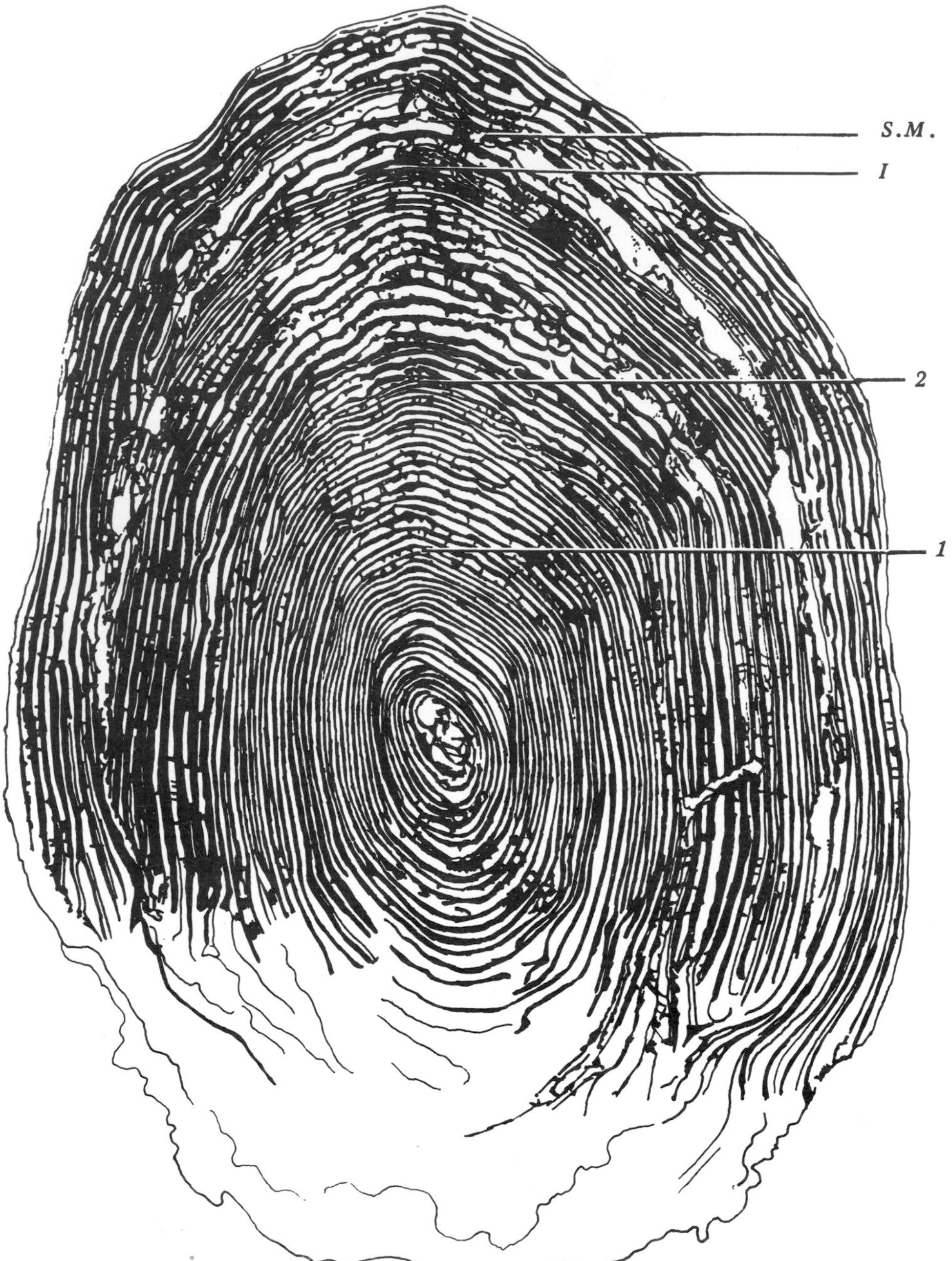

Fig. 13 Scale from an Atlantic feeding sea trout with the formula 2.1+ S.M.+ i.e. two parr years (1,2) followed by two sea winters (I;S.M.) of which one (S.M.) was occupied by a spawning mark. The slow rate of marine growth in this case is accompanied by a clearly defined annulus (winter band) during the first sea winter. This fish weighed 1.4 lb (0.64 kg).

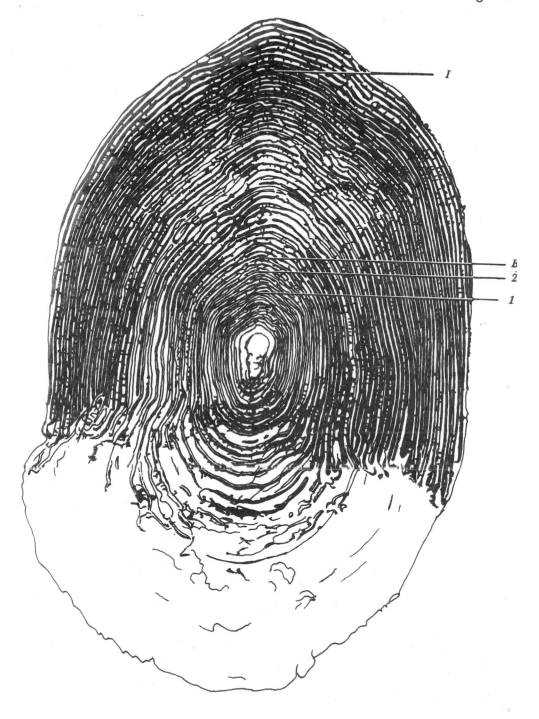

Fig. 14 *Scale from a sea trout feeding in the Irish Sea, with the formula 2.1+ (i.e. two freshwater (1,2) and one (I) sea winters). The rapid rate of circulus formation and the unclear annulus marking the end of the first sea winter (I) are noteworthy. This fish weighed 2.0 lb (0.9kg) at capture.*

reduced feeding and growth for a portion of the spring or summer.

Where food is not abundant scale formation can appear to be strongly seasonally influenced. Thus, along the Atlantic coast of Ireland poor winter growth is obvious (Fig. 13) whereas in the more abundant feeding conditions of the Irish Sea, sea winters can occasionally be difficult to decipher (Fig. 14) because marine growth is exuberant.

Stadia

The annual growth on a sea trout scale is recognised as the contrast between the very thin and narrowly-spaced circuli and the band of new 'summer' growth which succeeds them. In other words, a year's growth can only be confirmed as having taken place once a new year's development has commenced. Anything less is a *stadium*.

Stadia are often marginal on the scale but they may also be enclosed by subsequent growth. They consist of evenly laid down circuli which do not however end in an annulus. They represent a partial season's growth and, where they are bordered by later scale formation, this may expand into more vigorous growth as when, for example, the juvenile fish is feeding while moving downstream. The most common kind of stadia encountered in sea trout are the B-type increments which are formed in the spring of a fish's first descent to the sea. They are very similar to inconclusive freshwater growth in the previous year and they are replaced by true marine growth later (Fig. 15). Long estuaries, such as those of the rivers Moy and Foyle, contain trout which may display

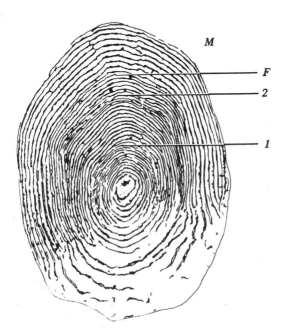

Fig. 15 Scale from a B type smolt with the formula 2.+; following two parr years (1,2) the fish stayed in freshwater for the spring of a third (F=B growth) then descended to the sea (M).

two distinguishable kinds of B-type growth (Fig. 16), before true marine growth is formed on the scale. B-type growth is known in salmon as well as trout and two phased B-type increments from the salmon of the River Adour in France have been described by R. Vibert. He attributes the inner B-type increment to summer river growth and the outer to summer estuary growth and this is taken to apply to trout also.

Very wide increments occasionally occur in association with the parr centre of sea trout scales (Fig. 17). But for the absence of a concluding annulus they would appear to be identical to a single year's growth. It is possible that some of the fish which display this growth pattern did not derive from spring descending smolts but from autumn migrating brown trout which left freshwater before scale formation for the year in question had been completed.

Sea trout spend a great deal of their time in the transitional waters of estuaries, in the course of passing from fresh water to the sea. Both Menzies and Nall appreciated that estuarine growth could play an important part in the life of the sea trout before its 'true migration' to sea.

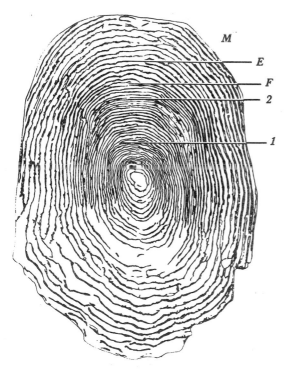

Fig. 16 Scale from a sea trout showing two phased B type growth, with the formula 2.+; following two parr years (1,2) the fish spent the spring of a third in freshwater (F = phase 1) then moved to richer feeding conditions for a short period (E = phase 2) before going to sea (M).

Fig. 17 Scale of an autumn migrating brown trout in the Burrishoole Fishery, Co. Mayo, with the formula 1.+ (or possibly 2.). Following a year's parr growth the fish passed another season in freshwater, descending however before the second winter annulus formed.

The essential nature of circulus formation during this period might have been deduced from the fact that 'during this period of estuarine life the food supply is more abundant' than further upstream. Yet Nall did not take B-type growth into account and, in the scales which he uses to illustrate his work, frequently interpreted a B-type increment as a full year's parr growth.

Spawning marks

Scales represent a massive investment in calcium by trout; as much as 40 per cent of the calcium contained in the body resides in the dermal skeleton. As soon as a trout ceases to feed resorption of this calcium commences, beginning at the periphery of the scale and presumably through the agency of cells which normally promote scale growth. Resorption (also termed absorption or erosion — the latter, incorrectly, implying an external mechanism) is heavily concentrated on the bony layer of the scale where its consequences are conspicuous.

Scale resorption has been shown to occur in clupeoid (herring-like) fish as well as in salmonids. However it is more marked in salmon and sea trout as a consequence of their life cycle which involves leaving marine feeding areas and moving into freshwater, a period in which they effectively cease to feed. An aggravating factor is the possible utilization of calcium in the formation of eggs and milt, a process which is believed to take place because the development of the ovary is associated with a fall in calcium content of the scales. Absorption commences as soon as marine feeding stops and is reversed only when the fish returns to sea and commences feeding again. It begins on the 'shoulder' of the scale and extends around its margin and is always more pronounced in male than in female trout.

Formation of a spawning mark results from two processes then, one the trout's ceasing to feed, the other its spawning activity. When a cessation of feeding coincides with spawning the effect would be expected to be traumatic. Salmon are known to cease feeding when they re-enter freshwater with the ultimate objective of spawning. On salmon, spawning exacts a great toll, and a very large proportion of them does not survive to spawn a second time. The scales of those that do bear unmistakable scars.

Fewer sea trout die after spawning, indeed sea trout live longer than salmon and may spawn on many more occasions. But each spawning also imposes considerable physiological stress whose effects are seen in the appearance of the fish and the spawning marks borne by its scales (Fig. 18). In brown trout on the other hand there is neither a heavy mortality or debilitation and reproduction usually leaves little or no discernible mark on the scales (Fig. 19). Nor does it in precocious male sea trout which spawn before they leave freshwater. And spawning marks may be

Fig. 18 Scale of a previously spawned sea trout of 9+ years with the formula 2.1+6 S.M.+; following a parr life of two yeras (1,2) the fish descended to the sea where, after a further winter (I), it spawned six times (1-6 S.M.) This sea-trout weighed 7 lb (3.2 kg) when captured.

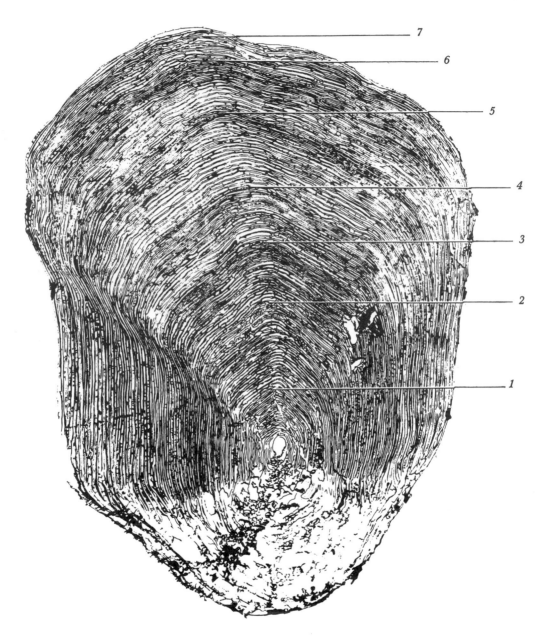

*Fig. 19   Scale from a lake trout of 7+ years; no discernible spawning mark.
This fish weighed 10 lb (4.5 kg) when captured.*

difficult to detect on post-smolts.

As far as scale formation and its associated physiology is concerned, sea trout have more in common with salmon than with brown trout. Thus, contrary to Hamish Stuart's arguments, there is a good basis for regarding salmon and sea trout as equals in the eyes of the law.

5

Freshwater Beginnings

Driving westwards through Co. Galway the River Corrib is crossed in Galway city centre. Some miles outside the city the terrain changes; quite abruptly the lush, flat limestone grasslands change to hilly, peaty, barren Connemara. The surrounding agriculture has become poorer and brown trout fisheries have been replaced by the white or sea-run form. For Kingsmill Moore, an innovative angler and a keen observer, Co. Galway was a well known area. His comments on the occurrence of sea trout there have general relevance to the distribution of this fish in other parts of Britain and Ireland:

> Nearly every river in Ireland contains white trout, but they seem to prefer acid water to alkaline and when they do enter a limestone stream they take the first opportunity of escaping up a more acid tributary. Galway Bay gives an interesting example of their preferences. Its northern shore is a succession of one famous white trout fishery after another. At its eastern end flows in the Corrib River which drains a lake larger than all the white trout lakes put together. A few white trout — and those often large — enter the Corrib River but I never caught a white trout in the lake, nor do I know anyone who did. Although many of the streams which feed Corrib rise within a mile of the headwaters of the streams which feed the white trout fisheries, Corrib lies chiefly on limestone, and so has alkaline water, and the white trout lakes lie on peat and granite which makes them acid.

Had a scientist and not an observant angler remarked on the occurrence of sea trout his conclusions might not have been so concise or accurate. Scientists record animal presence without necessarily taking into account the numbers of a species involved. This approach places inordinate stress on rarities, very often to the exclusion of more common species and events which it is felt are not worth noting. For many years the only recorded fish species from the Bull Island, an area of considerable scientific interest close to Dublin, was the sea horse, one specimen of which had been collected there. Many other fish species abounded but nobody felt it worthwhile to list them. Sea trout are known to undertake very long migrations so that plotting the distribution of newsworthy individuals which have strayed away from the common run could give a very false impression.

An analysis of sea trout occurrence in fresh waters in Ireland, based on regular runs of the fish rather than occasional records (the kind of information which an angler would consult in choosing a place to fish) confirms that sea trout have a maritime distribution, occurring in the smaller catchments and sub-catchments adjacent to the coast (Fig. 20). Sea trout come into all estuaries, including those of the largest rivers, to feed, and they may even dash into the lower fresh water reaches of those rivers but regular runs of the fish are confined to smaller catchments.

The reasons for smaller catchments being favoured is probably the small size of these salmonids. Atlantic salmon ascend to distances above the tide which are proportional to their size. The largest rivers like the Rhine were, before pollution and overfishing decimated them, populated by large salmon which spent three and four winters at sea before returning to spawn (when they weighed up to 40 lb (18 kg)). Perhaps only fish of that size could generate sufficient power to penetrate so far inland.

Although the information on sea trout occurrence recounted here refers to Ireland it can be taken to have application elsewhere. The kind of river frequented by regular migrations of these fish is up to 30 miles (approximately 50 km) in length; streams of between 10 and 15 miles (16 and 24 km) long are particularly favoured. Catchments containing river channels of these lengths are small and most numerous in the hilly terrain of western Britain and Ireland. The more gentle topography of the east coast is drained by a combination of larger rivers and few small streams. In the larger catchments sea trout inhabit the lower tributaries but they rarely stray far up the main channels. Its predilection for small rivers and their concentration on the western seaboard has given sea trout the reputation of being a mainly western form of trout.

Another feature of the western mountainous districts is the materials of which they are composed. Water which flows over granite and other igneous rocks is poor in dissolved bone-making chemicals, often by a factor of five to ten times lower than limestone water, and it is indeed water of this kind — technically described as oligotrophic — which is the stronghold of the fish. That fact was recognised by R.A. Chrystal who characterised the freshwaters producing sea trout in Scotland in the following terms:

> ... It will be found that (they) are usually rapid, rocky and barren, the typical small rill of the west coast of Scotland. In these the sea trout are very numerous in proportion to the size of the river ... in rivers of this type practically the whole stock of trout is migratory ... Theoretically then, if there existed a river so rich in feeding that it could support all its own trout, and grow them to a large size and superlative condition, it would produce no sea trout at all, for the simple reason that its trout would not *require* to migrate ...

Fig. 20 (left) The distribution of limestone in Ireland and (right) catchments and sub-catchments known to support reproducing sea trout populations.

It is worth pausing to consider the above statement in some depth. In the Irish context which has been examined in greater detail than the British, limestone river basins tend to be larger than catchments on acidic rocks. This is a result of limestone being more centrally distributed in the country (Fig. 20). The flatter topography associated with the limestone means that rivers flowing over it are longer from source to mouth and sea trout may not be physically able to undertake the journey from the tide to suitable spawning gravels upstream; that is a statement of the problem as seen from the seaward end. Alternatively trout which breed in the headwaters of such a system may undertake their feeding migration to the waters of the main channel where there is adequate food to sustain their growth and development. Very probably both of these explanations contribute to the paucity of sea-run trout in limestone rivers.

Implicit in Chrystal's appraisal of the situation is a belief which is also current in scientific circles that sea trout are *made* rather than *born*; that competitive pressures force them down to the sea. From what has already been said it is the balance or imbalance between what can be termed 'nursery' and 'feeding' areas that would appear to have the deciding role. In other words if the main channel or associated lakes of a freshwater system are insufficiently large to accommodate trout produced in their inflowing tributaries the fish would be pressurised to migrate out of the system and *vice versa*.

This contention is supported by the occasional existence of *maritime brown trout systems*. Three are known in Connemara: Gorumna, Aughrusbeg and Camus Eighter (Fig. 21). All are within 3 miles (5 km) of the sea and all have clear access for migratory fish and yet such fish are rarely captured there. Within all the Connemara sea trout fisheries some brown trout are taken in association with sea-run fish. This is not unusual because the two forms co-exist in all sea trout systems. In the three small catchments referred to here brown trout constitute the vast majority if not all of the catch. And whereas in the majority of sea trout fisheries brown liveried trout of up to 4 oz (100 g) are often captured, the brown trout in these maritime systems are between 1 and something over 2 lb (0.5 to 1 kg), or approximately comparable in weight with sea trout. Most significant, the three little catchments are regularly fished for brown rather than sea trout.

Some other systems in the Connemara Fishery District yield a large proportion of their catch in the form of brown trout. All of these systems are underlain by similar bedrock but a close examination reveals some intriguing differences between them and neighbouring sea trout-producing systems. In some of the maritime brown trout catchments, either there is a relatively short channel length (relative to the lake surface) or else the feeder streams are slow, sluggish and often overgrown by vegetation like the pond weed (*Potamogeton*). In these conditions spawning and nursery area is greatly restricted or non-existent and, it must be owned, the

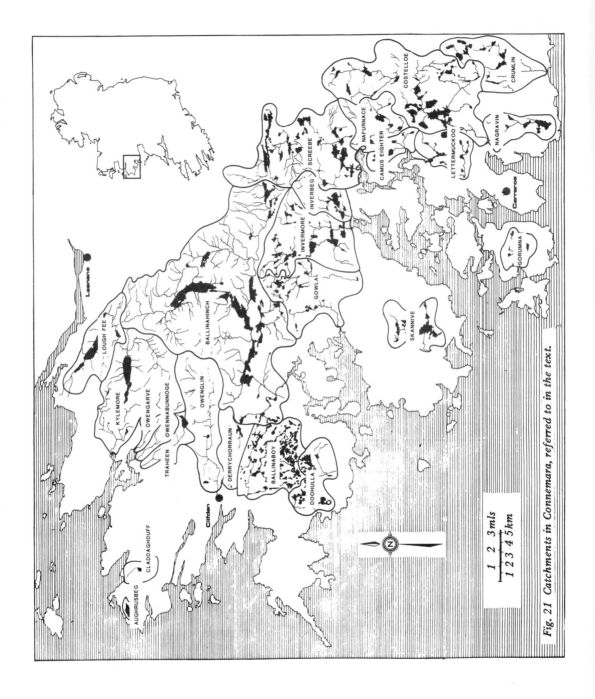

Fig. 21 Catchments in Connemara, referred to in the text.

spawning places for trout in some of the catchments listed remain to be discovered. Any output of trout that are produced there must be very low and it seems likely that all such fish are easily accommodated in the lakes to which the nursery waters drain. Thus, it might be said, the trout produced in systems of this kind have no need or drive to migrate any further.

Biology of sea trout producing waters

The typical sea trout-producing stream is acidic rather than alkaline and it may be very small, as narrow as 12 in (30 cm). It consists of a succession of pools and riffles (broken waters) and its proportion of standing or stagnant waters overgrown with aquatic vegetation is small. Where rooted, submerged, floating or emergent flowering plants (Angiosperms) become established, salmonids will be comparatively few.

The small streams most productive of salmonids contain little obvious vegetation apart from the aquatic moss *Fontinalis antipyretica* although there is a diverse microscopic flora consisting of one-celled algae, filamentous forms (such as *Spirogyra*) and more complex types like the red alga *Batrachospermum*. The algal flora occurring in these moorland streams in Britain and Ireland is of a kind widespread in arctic tundra areas. In winter when growth of the algae has slowed or ceased and spate waters have torn any trailing filaments away, the stony substratum will appear clear and free of vegetation. But in the high temperatures and low water levels of midsummer algal growth will often appear as a mossy green scum on the stream-bed.

Plants are primary producers, manufacturing their own food, and vegetable material is the basis of every animal food chain. Stream-dwelling algae play a part in this although in terms of quantity they are less important than other kinds of vegetation originating outside the stream. In wooded valleys leaves of trees arc a source of nutrients, and from the moorlands which surround many sea trout fisheries, the dead leaves of the purple moor grass (*Molinia caerulea*) are blown into streams at the end of the year when the plant has died back. Plant material from outside the stream is in time broken down by bacteria and consumed by invertebrates living in the water.

The invertebrate animals comprise a wide range of species, the majority of them insects, although there are worms and crustacean species also. Anglers will probably be familiar with many of the most important insect groups (taxa), the larvae of sedges (Trichoptera), mayflies (Ephemeroptera) and stoneflies (Plecoptera). In terms of numbers of species the best represented groups in the stream fauna are the non-biting midges (chironomids) of which there are perhaps sixty common species in sea trout-producing waters. Because these organisms are very small they are important to the young stages of the fish, the fry and small parr. The olive nymphs are a group of mayfly species which are also very numerous in the smaller streams frequented by the young stages of trout.

Salmonids are exclusively carnivorous, in common with the majority of British and Irish freshwater fish. Trout start feeding before the yolk sac is completely absorbed when their choice of food is confined to tiny crustaceans such as copepods and cladocerans (water fleas). These occur abundantly in lake waters and, where there are nursery streams between lakes, the tiny fish often cluster at the lake outflows snapping up the small planktonic organisms as they drift downstream. Hatchery managers appreciated the value of lake plankton as a hatchery food and before the advent of modern pelleted foods it used to be standard practice to concentrate the invertebrates in fine-meshed nets to feed the early fry.

To be most efficient a predator will select as large or abundant a prey item as it can cope with; capturing food can be expensive in energy terms if prey are too small or sparse to justify the effort. Neither must the maximum width of a prey item exceed the throat width of a trout predator and in ideal feeding circumstances (where there is a wide choice of prey) the size of predator and prey will be related.

Cladocerans and copepods do not hold their appeal for the growing trout for long. They are demoted in its feeding affections after perhaps a couple of weeks when small olive nymphs and chironomid larvae are consumed in greater quantity. As the fish grows further its feeding behaviour becomes more varied and adaptable until specific choices of food are displayed at certain times. Different invertebrates will be selected in daylight to those consumed in the hours of darkness. And, to maximise its feeding efficiency, the trout will learn to feast on a particular stage of the life cycle of a particular invertebrate species, like an emerging mayfly, when it is available in large numbers.

Trout growth

Trout feed in order to grow and that growth can be described as a series of steps (alevin − fry − parr − smolt). The parr phase is of longest duration and it may not necessarily end in a recognisable smolt stage. The parr stage can last as long as five years − although examples of this duration are few in Britain, fewer in Ireland − or the necessary growth could be accomplished in as little as one year. The majority of sea trout 'smolts' are two years of age; the average or *mean smolt age* is between two and three years. Within these limits it can vary a lot and that fact can have an important bearing on the size of sea trout stocks and the numbers available to the rod and net.

Watching juvenile salmonids in a hatchery pond gives a very false impression of their nature. They swim about in the still waters and congregate under the automatic feeding dispenser. In the running waters of nursery streams they are fiercely territorial, each defending a small patch from which all intruders are driven. To lose one's territory means being displaced to find another or starve. The bigger the feeding territory one holds the better the feeding and the faster one grows. This in turn facilitates occupation of an even larger feeding area.

Trout spawn before salmon and their young emerge from the gravel before those of the larger species. Hence they seize the most productive feeding territory first and this start in life gives trout an advantage which salmon cannot overtake. Co-existing juvenile salmon are smaller at any age than trout. Given their fluctuating fortunes in choice of territory it is understandable that at any time there is considerable variation in the length attained by juvenile trout of the same age.

The lengths of two year old smolts (as identified by scale-reading) typically average 3 in (7.6 cm) with a variation from 1.4 to 5.7 in (3.6 to 14.5 cm) at the end of their first freshwater year. For three year old smolts the average length is 2.4 in (6.1 cm) with a range from 1.3 to 4.6 in (3.3 to 11.7 cm) at the end of their first freshwater year. Thus, between these two smolt classes (a group of a particular age at smolti-fication is referred to as a *class*) there is much overlap. There will be some overlap also between the lengths attained by two year smolts at the end of their first and second years.

If within a stock of trout five smolt classes were represented then there could be fifteen age groups in the stream:

Smolt age		Parr years		
5	4	3	2	1
4	3	2	1	
3	2	1		
2	1			
1				

Most would have overlapping dimensions at particular ages, although we could assume that one year smolts would on average be longer at one year than two year old smolts at that age, etc. With all this variation the prediction of its age at migration of a particular juvenile would be almost impossible.

It has already been observed that smolt dimensions in a particular catchment remain constant. In other words, once a threshold size is achieved by the trout in that catchment they will migrate. Obviously an older smolt will have taken longer to reach the requisite length than a younger and faster growing individual.

In freshwater juvenile trout can be shown to grow in response to environmental conditions. Temperature is a significant regulator and the average length reached by trout in a particular stream can be related to the temperature prevailing there during the year. When temperature is favourable, growth is rapid and the average length of the entire trout stock is high. Several smolt classes will eventually emerge from the stream but the mean smolt age (i.e. the average age of juvenile trout going to sea for the first time) will tend to be low. If, that is, temperatures are favourable. That is not to say they should be high. Excessive heat may inhibit growth which frequently ceases in trout during midsummer; it may even kill the fish. Of greater consequence is the period for which a certain medium temperature prevails.

Specific studies have demonstrated the relationship between trout growth and water temperature but it is difficult to relate these very accurately to the overall consequences for sea trout growth and production because such data are collected only in special experimental circumstances and over a limited geographical area. Instead we have to search elsewhere for regularly collected data to indicate freshwater conditions for juvenile trout. This is by no means an uncommon approach in biology. Some of the most satisfactory work on predicting stock size of sardines has been carried out using climatic data derived from studies of tree rings! In this case nothing so exotic is required. The temperature of small nursery streams is in approximate equilibrium with the ambient air temperature, so a knowledge of the air temperature gives a crude indication of the conditions favourable to trout growth.

A statistic of wide application in agriculture is the length of the grass-growing season. Data relating to it have been collected in Britain and Ireland and although the information covers about thirty-five years in Ireland much longer records are available for the United Kingdom. There are some drawbacks in the use of these statistics, even for the purpose for which they were collected. Their interpretation is uncertain, because their precise relevance to grass growth is disputed by experts. And it must be said that the method of collecting these statistics has changed over the years.

Reservations aside, the grass-growing season is a useful indicator, if nothing more, to the trends in juvenile trout production. In south-west Ireland the annual growing season over a period averaged 330 days whereas on the coast of the north of Scotland it was 240 days. The mean smolt age of trout is consistently higher in Scotland than in Ireland. As one travels north therefore the growing season shortens. But at any one place its length may change from one year to another. The precise climatic regulator for this alteration is not known but several studies have linked length of the growing season with sun spot numbers so the mechanism is assumed to be climatic rather than a local weather effect, and it is thought to operate on a global scale.

In the earlier years of this century the trend in length of growing seasons was increasing but that tendency has now reversed. Between the mid 1970s when growing seasons were long and the mid 1980s their reduction is quite marked and the loss of grass-growing time has been approximately one calendar month per year.

The effects of changing length of growing season on sea trout catches will be considered later; for the moment we must look at its influence on the output of trout from fresh water.

Trout spawn in very shallow water, as far upstream as there is water to take them. They produce a very large number of eggs so there are more than enough young fish to populate the streams. As they grow their increasing food requirements oblige them to disperse over the stream bed and their increasing size drives them into deeper waters. In common with all stream dwelling salmonids they are fiercely territorial.

The result of their competitive behaviour is a constant downstream movement of juvenile trout which occupy the smallest spawning streams for only their first year of life. Later they move into the larger river or even lake waters to complete freshwater growth there. This is a useful behavioural adaptation which reduces contact between younger fry and the older parr which would consume them. However the speed with which river waters are vacated is dependent on the rate at which the trout grow and so, because stream-bed space is finite and limited, the rate of growth determines the throughput of juveniles in a nursery system. Hence, any curtailment of growing conditions slows trout development and causes something of a bottleneck in the production of juvenile fish.

The process described can be observed only where juvenile trout are counted as they leave a freshwater system. Such counts indicate that a gradual build-up in juvenile output coincides with lengthening growing seasons but that once growing conditions begin to decline the output of fish becomes erratic: high and low in alternate years but with a downward tendency. In the Burrishoole fishery in western Ireland where migrating salmonids are continuously monitored, the loss of one month annually in the growing season since the mid 1970s has been accompanied by a reduction of one-quarter in the numbers of juvenile trout going to sea.

Descent to the sea

Trout forsake their rivers and lakes for the sea on two occasions in the year. The spring smolt run is the better known of these. Small silvered trout are its participants. But in the autumn there is an exodus, which may be as great, of small brown liveried trout.

The autumn run consists of trout younger by one winter than the smolts of the following spring so some scientists have been inclined to regard them as precursors of the exodus the following year. That conclusion might be tempered by considering the reasons why the autumn descent takes place. It is after all a movement of trout which are smaller than smolts and, because they are not silvered, they are not so well pre-adapted to survive in salt water.

Autumn descending salmonids have been described as 'nomads' and their downstream movement has been explained as a search for feeding territory after displacement from other parts of the stream bed. As they move downstream searching for another feeding place the small parr are chased away by the already firmly ensconced territory holders.

In autumn adult sea and brown trout move upstream with the objective of spawning. They can be voracious and although the feeding of sea-run trout slows down or ceases in the river their kelts have been known to gorge themselves on juvenile fish. A tactical withdrawal in the face of this invasion would be a good survival strategy by young trout and that may be the explanation for the downstream movement of the parr. Alternatively the two reasons might combine to explain their downstream migration. Whatever the cause these small trout are not best adapted for the sea. Some of them undoubtedly survive there, and recruit into the sea-run stock the following summer when they appear similar to the post-smolts of that year. It is however very likely that a large proportion of this cohort perishes.

So trout can migrate either at the end of a year's growth which slows and finishes in the autumn months, or as early running smolts the following spring. If they are less than the critical size for smoltification in early spring they can grow a little more in freshwater and then go seawards later that same year. Juveniles with this extra freshwater growth on their scales are the later descending or B-type smolts. B-type growth takes them to a migratory size (on average it slightly exceeds the length of A-type fish at migration) and B-type growth is made by slower developing trout (Fig. 22). B-type growth is therefore compensatory, bringing fish to a necessary migrating size, later than A-types. Younger smolts make a greater amount of B-growth than older fish and the incidence of fish displaying it on the scales decreases as one ascends the smolt classes; that is, a greater percentage of one than four year smolts have made B-type growth.

B-type growth is a partial season's development whose full significance is obscured by the 'mean smolt age' statistic. It would also seem to be associated with the distance a juvenile must move downstream to the sea. Smolts feed rapaciously in the course of this journey. The clearest examples of B-type growth come from rivers with sizeable estuaries and the few cases of two phased B-type scales which have been recorded in Ireland originated from the Rivers Moy and Foyle whose estuaries are very long (about 5 miles; 8 km).

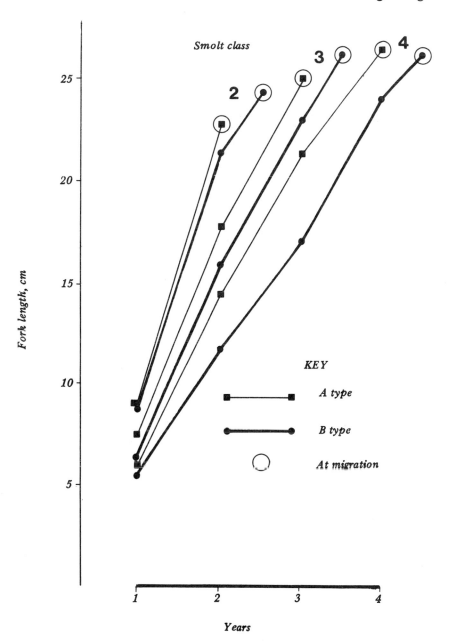

Fig. 22 Length at age of A and B-type smolts of three age classes.

6

Trout in the Sea

The maxim that the female of a species is more long-lived than the male is often cited in animal biology. This is as true in human populations (the higher proportion of female to male old age pensioners) as it is in trout. But in trout its effects are visible at a very early stage. Among smolts the nearest approach to a one to one ratio of females to males occurs in the youngest classes, the one and two year olds. Thereafter as the age of the fish increases, the males thin out.

There are valid reasons for this rule. Being successful biologically means surviving long enough to reproduce and pass on one's genetic material to the next generation. The male gametes or milt of salmon and trout are far less bulky and require much less tissue than the female's eggs. Males can manufacture milt at a smaller size and therefore a younger age and, to further emphasise the versatility of a male of smaller dimensions than the female, one of the former might well serve several of the latter in the course of a single spawning season. The larger size of the mature female sea trout is needed to excavate a deep redd — the male does not assist with this task. And a larger female can, and possibly must, migrate further to richer feeding in order to consume sufficient food to form the eggs. So on average a mature female will be older than a mature male. Indeed males in a sea trout spawning population need not be sea-run.

Precocious male parr are usually the larger, faster growing members of a particular year class. For example trout aged less than one year, encountered during a survey of spawning fish in Connemara, averaged 2.8 in (7.1 cm) in length. Males of that age which had matured — had running milt — averaged 3.7 in (9.4 cm). In the previous chapter it was seen that the rate of growth of fish in freshwater is greatly influenced by the environmental conditions which regulate the length of the growing season; the point was also made that trout lay an excessive number of eggs to ensure that there are adequate numbers of juveniles. Occasionally there may be too few spawning adults to ensure every feeding territory is occupied. This is true of Atlantic salmon which in recent years have been heavily exploited. In those circumstances there is more than enough feeding territory to go round and the young fish grow faster as a result. A large proportion of juvenile males will mature before completing freshwater growth and these fish will have an opportunity to reproduce without having to go to sea and make up the necessary growth to reach mature size there. This is a useful adaptation because going to sea is a risky business entailing a high mortality of the fish that undertake the migration. For a hard pressed and depleted population staying at home and being able to breed there has obvious advantages.

A tendency towards residency has been identified as a behavioural adaptation of male sea trout. Among sea-run fish therefore the ratio of females to males could be expected to be more than one. The preponderance of females is not fixed and may vary from one year to the next in the same stock. A factor likely to modify the ratio is the mean smolt age. The higher the mean smolt age, the older the migrating juvenile trout would be and the more females the population would contain. Among post-smolts, ratios in the order of 1.4 females to one male are often reported.

Where ratios of the order of 1.4 occur in the post-smolt or earliest sea age group, the sex ratio of the entire stock, including older sea age groups, is higher. In the sea trout stock of a western Irish sea lough investigated in 1981 the ratio of female to male trout was one to one among trout of less than about 8 in (20 cm) in length. No males of more than 16 in (40 cm) were captured and only 10 per cent of the fish of between 12 to 16 in (30 to 40 cm) were males.

Reflecting the ratios described, the average age of males is invariably lower than that of female trout. During a survey of spawning trout in Connemara female sea-run fish had an average sea age of 2.36 years as against 2.24 years in the males. A similar investigation of spawning fish in the Cummeragh system in Co. Kerry indicated the average sea age of the males was 0.93 years against 1.35 years in the females. In both surveys the mean river age of the males was lower than in the females. In the Connemara fish males averaged 2.24 years and females 2.36 while in the Cummeragh survey males had an average freshwater life of 2.28 and females 2.55 years.

Wanderings in the sea

The main descent of juvenile sea trout — as smolts — takes place in the spring months when they make a slow downstream progress. The majority migrate between March and May but small numbers of smolts continue to pass downstream into the summer months. If a sea lough or a sizeable estuary intervenes between fresh and sea water the fish may spend one or two months in it before continuing to fully marine conditions; some sea trout possibly do not go any further seawards. The migrations of sea trout can be technically described as *diplochrone* or having two activity periods, descending to the sea in spring and returning to freshwater in the autumn for spawning.

Insufficient work has been done to enable a comprehensive appraisal of sea trout movements in the sea but some general statements are feasible following a number of separate investigations made in European countries. Precisely where sea trout go from specific catchments to feed is unknown and much of the data obtained over the years probably reflects the distribution of suitable fishing effort rather than the abundance of the fish.

Earlier workers like Nall and Menzies reported heavy concentrations of sea trout off the Norfolk and Suffolk coasts and heavy catches by Dutch and German vessels on the Danish and Dutch coasts. Sea trout were particularly associated with the herring fisheries of the east Scottish coast. Apart from the fact that juvenile herrings are an acceptable food to sea trout and that the two species frequently occur together for this reason, the gear used for the capture of herrings would also be suitable for sea trout. For the same reasons sea trout have been reported in trawl catches of sprats from southern Ireland.

Several reports refer to the more inshore distribution of post-smolt sea trout and the occurrence of older age categories further out in the ocean. Post-smolts are known to form large aggregations and to invade estuaries other than their own. The very often brief first migration can end with their re-entry to freshwater within two to three months.

More recent and intensive Scottish investigations of sea trout migration suggest that the fish fan out from their natal river. There are numerous examples of individuals moving in excess of 65 miles (about 100 km) along the coast and some may even travel more than 300 miles (about 500 km). The earlier returns of post-smolts to freshwater — of which there may be several in their year of first descent — are not necessarily to their river of origin. This point has considerable implications for the management of sea trout particularly of those stocks exploited as post-smolts because the beneficiary may not be the nursery river system. An argument could be made in these circumstances for managing the stocks on a *regional* rather than a *single catchment* basis. As the fish age their return to freshwater becomes more purposeful, and genetic studies reveal that there is little admixture of stocks of spawning age, enabling individual populations to retain specific biochemical and physical characteristics.

Certain stocks may display preferences for definite feeding grounds. Sea trout tagged off the East Anglian coast were recaptured as post-smolts within the area of release and as older trout further north, suggesting discreet feeding places at these two stages of the life cycle.

Work on the sea trout of the Indalsalven River in Sweden confirms that older trout home more accurately than younger and that larger smolts survive better than smaller. Tagging and recapture experiments on these stocks suggested that the majority of the fish stayed within 13 miles (about 20 km) of the river mouth and only a few migrated 125 miles (about 200 km) or more. However the distance of migration may alter from one year to another, possibly in response to the availability of food. The homing ability of older trout was found to be as well developed as in grilse, a result of their experience, maturity and conditioning.

Additional work carried out on Swedish sea trout has shown that some stocks are adapted to migrations in coastal waters and others to journeys in the open sea, the implication being that homing ability is at least partially genetically determined. Orientation and homing mechanisms of these fish have been deduced by a series of experiments in which the vision and smelling capabilities of the trout were selectively impaired. Juvenile trout and grilse orientate in the same way, by *chemotaxis* or smell. Adult fish use *phototaxis* or vision in the home river. The two mechanisms operate in the same fish at different phases of its life cycle. Imprinting for smell occurs in the estuary and the operation of this and the sight orientation mechanism depend on the physiological state of the fish.

Marine food

As with the feeding of parr in freshwater, the larger the prey item with which a sea trout can cope, the more rewarding the feeding effort. However the diet of sea trout is very variable, depending on the circumstances in which they find themselves and they display great adaptability at surviving in places which produce few fodder fish.

Every investigation of marine feeding by sea trout to date has identified sand eel *Ammodytes* and sprat *Sprattus* as major elements of the diet. Sand eels and sprats are widely distributed in western Europe (Figs. 23 and 24) and both are fished industrially, largely for fishmeal. Both are shoaling species and could be described as *bait fish*, feeding mainly on small planktonic organisms such as copepods. Sprats form large over-wintering companies in coastal waters, bays and estuaries where they are exploited using purse seines and midwater trawls. Sea trout, feeding on the shoals, are frequently captured in the course of these operations. If the distribution of sprats is predominantly inshore, sand eels are fished further from land. There are five species in British waters of which one, *A. marinus*, comprises the bulk of the catch. This species can be locally abundant close to shore. Until recently in the Irish Sea there was a transient fishery for sand eels but Fig. 23 understates the ubiquity of these fodder species.

In the Irish Sea sprats and sand eels form intermixed shoals. A larger sand eel species, *Hyperoplus lanceolatus*, preys on *A. marinus* and so occurs with it. Although these three species are not the only recorded prey of sea trout, which will gorge themselves on a range of invertebrate species, such as spawning and readily available nereid worms, the three fish species are the prey most frequently recorded. The fodder shoals

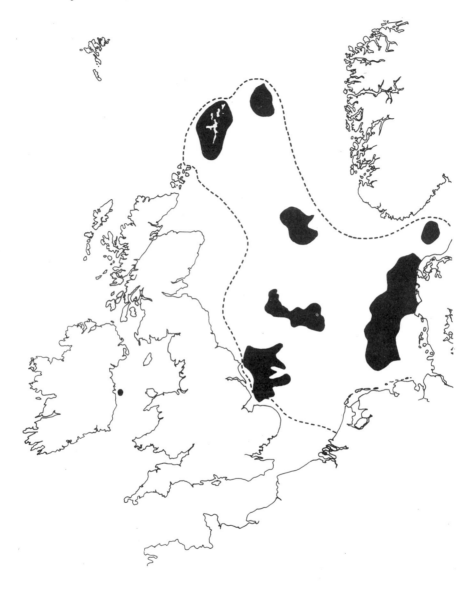

Fig. 23 The distribution of sand eel fishing areas in north western Europe; the main areas are indicated in black, the broken line marks the limit of secondary fishing. Intensity of fishing can be regarded as proportional to the abundance of the fish.

Fig. 24 The distribution of sprat fishing areas in north western Europe. The main fishing areas are marked in black and the broken line indicates the probable limits of the species.

occur in shallow inshore waters and, in summer an important component of their diet is the tiny planktonic larva of cirripedes (barnacles), particularly that of *Balanus balanoides* (Fig. 25). Barnacles are familar as numerous encrusting but insignificant animals on rocky shorelines. Their larvae which are about 0.04 in (1 mm) long are even less conspicuous.

Where fodder fish are locally abundant, gorging themselves on barnacle larvae close inshore, sea trout patrol the shoreline snapping up the small fish. Sand eels seem especially suitable as prey and where sea trout were observed to feed most abundantly the older sea-run fish concentrated on sand eel prey of more than one year of age while the post-smolts, recently descended from freshwater, consumed sand eels of less than one year old. Thus, post-smolt and older sea trout were not in competition for the same food resource although they fed on the same species. The degree of success of these feeding trout was judged on the basis of the amount of food in their stomachs. In the midst of plenty some fish contained food which weighed up to 10 per cent of their body weight. They were bloated and the consequences of rich feeding were obvious in their scale formation and their shape about which more will be said later. Because this kind of exuberant feeding was observed in the Irish Sea, although not confined to that region, it is described as *Irish*

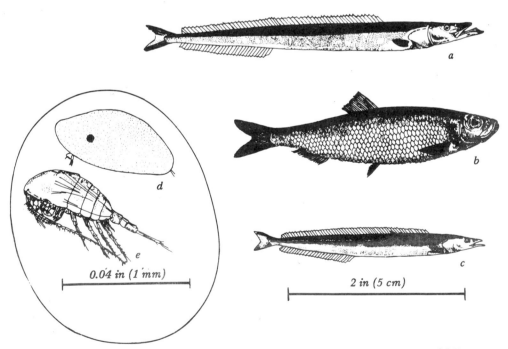

Fig. 25   The chief constituents of the sea trout food chain in the Irish Sea: (a) Hyperoplus lanceolatus, *(b)* Sprattus sprattus, *(c)* Ammodytes marinus; *inset: two important elements in the food chain of the fodder fishes, (d) the cypris stage of a cirripede and (e) the copepod* Temora longicornis.

Sea feeding and the trout which show symptoms of the kind of over-indulgence involved are referred to as *Irish Sea type* fish.

The alternative kind of feeding (and there may be intermediate sorts) has been described from Atlantic waters in Scotland and Ireland. These, like the oligotrophic or poor freshwater lakes which are distributed over the same kinds of bedrock, can be barren and unproductive. It is a tribute to the mutable feeding behaviour of sea trout that they adjust to such penurious circumstances.

Some sprats and sand eels occur everywhere and sea trout utilise them in Atlantic waters but their menu there is longer and the quantities of each organism ingested are small; in other words the diet shows great diversity. This diversity implies that the feeding behaviour must be frequently adjusted in the Atlantic for the trout to subsist on prey of tiny size and low numbers.

A part of the species list recorded from the stomachs of sea trout captured in Co. Donegal is shown in Fig. 26. There the most numerous fish species was the three-spined stickleback, *Gasterosteus aculeatus*, which outnumbered sprats and sand eels. The sand goby, *Pomatoschistus minutus*, and sand smelt, *Atherina presbyter*, can occur in large numbers in summer but the other fish are likely to have been selected as individuals rather than as members of a shoal. They occurred in the trout as single examples and not with ten or twenty other members of their species as happens in the case of shoal fish. The choice of plaice, *Pleuronectes platessa*, is unusual because it is a bottom dweller and the trout is a mid-water and surface feeder, but in shallow water bottom dwelling (benthic) foods are obviously vulnerable when times are hard. Fish like the pollack, *Pollachius pollachius*, and the bib, *Trisopterus luscus*, are common in-shore species which have a fairly solitary way of life. They would have to be searched out individually, which is an energy consuming business, but at least they make a decent meal once located. This could not be said of the majority of the remainder of the organisms illustrated in Fig. 26, with the exception of the lug worm, *Arenicola marina*. The insects are very small and all are terrestrial species which are blown off-shore and into the water. In the sea lough from which these results were recorded fly fishing for sea trout is practised but the high numbers — though low volumes — of insects in the diet is not peculiar to this place.

The incidence of shellfish (molluscs) in the diet reveals a real effort to seek out prey. These animals are slow moving at best and would not be expected to make the fast or sudden movements betraying their presence which one associates with attracting the attention of a trout.

By far the greatest volume of trout food is supplied in Atlantic waters by small crustaceans, notably those of the sand hopper or sand flea type. In scientific terminology they belong to the group known as amphipods. Other crustaceans, the shrimp-like *Praunus flexuosa*, *Nebalia bipes* and the isopod *Idotea*, are shown in Fig. 26 for completeness. But

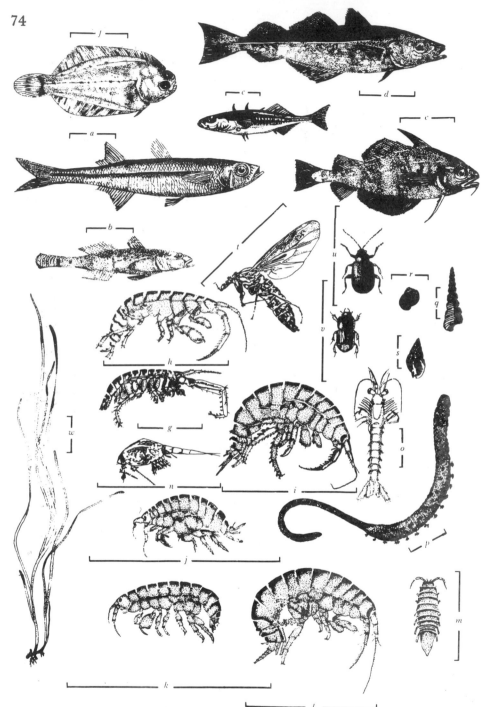

Fig. 26 Constituents of the sea trout food chain in an Atlantic sea lough: Fish: (a) Atherina presbyter, *(b)* Pomotoschistus minutus, *(c)* Gasterosteus aculeatus, *(d)* Polla- chius pollachius, *(e)* Trisopterus luscus, *(f)* Pleuronectes platessa; *Crustaceans: (g)* Coro- phium volutator, *(h)* Amphitoe rubricata, *(i)* Gammarus zaddachi, *(j)* Bathyporeia *sp.,* *(k)* Hyale *sp., (l)* Chaetogammarus *sp., (m)* Idotea *sp., (n)* Nebalia bipes, *(o)* Praunus flexuosa; *Polychaeta (worms): (p)* Arenicola marina; *Mollusca (snails): (q)* Turritella *sp.,* *(r)* Littorina littorea, *(s)* Nassarius *sp., Insects: (t)* Dilophus *sp., (u)* Lochmaea *sp.,* *(v)* Aphodius *sp., (w) Angiosperma (grass):* Zostera *sp. All scale lines represent 1 cm.*

amphipods in Atlantic sea loughs form a sizeable proportion of the total amount of available animal life and various creatures other than sea trout depend on them for food.

The cleaner estuaries of British and Irish coasts are characterised by the presence of the plant *Zostera* (eel grass) which is a member of the family Naidaceae. It produces seeds and flowers like any terrestrial grass species. In the autumn it dies back and disintegrates through the agency of bacteria which invade the plant tissue. In Denmark *Zostera*, which has died back, has been identified as an important food resource on which an entire food chain is based. Sea trout have been known to consume the seeds of *Zostera* and that, for a carnivore, represents either an error of judgement or extreme pangs of hunger!

It is not difficult to conclude that sea trout on the Atlantic sea-board arc not over-nourished. Their gaunt aspect we will examine later when the Condition of sea trout in the sea is described. In individual sea trout captured on the Atlantic coastline the stomach was rarely completely filled and the largest quantities of food never amounted to more than 3.5 per cent of the total weight of the fish.

Marine growth

The sea growth of trout expresses itself in two ways, extension of length and alteration in weight. Once growth commences it is rapid though not as fast as for salmon (Fig. 27). The amount of growth made during its first descent to the sea is largely dependent on the size of the migrating juvenile. Some general statements are feasible. The larger smolts, exemplified by the Cummeragh fish, extend by 40 to 50 per cent of their smolt length during their first migration to sea whereas smaller smolts may lengthen by 90 per cent. The end of the first summer's growth is usually an evening-up process and trout of this age average about 12.6 in (32 cm). Like all average measurements this one is subject to a degree of variability but the majority of fish of this age fall between 11 and 14 in (28 to 36 cm). The main reasons for variation are, first, the age of the 'smolt': older smolts are on average larger than younger ones and larger juveniles tend to hold that slight advantage over their smaller fellows in later growth. Secondly, richer marine feeding can slightly benefit the fish with an increase in size. Sea trout from the Irish Sea are thus marginally longer at the end of the first sea sojourn than their equivalents from the Atlantic. Thereafter length at sea age conforms to one of two patterns. It must be understood that this is a very simplified account of growth but within these limitations the two patterns would be:

	Irish Sea		Atlantic	
Sea year	*in*	*cm*	*in*	*cm*
First	13.4	34	12.6	32
Second	19.7	50	15.8	40
Third	24.8	63	18.9	48
Fourth	28.3	72	21.3	54

Here the conventions used to describe the kinds of sea feeding encountered are employed. Sea trout from the Irish Sea and from Poland would belong to much the same grouping.

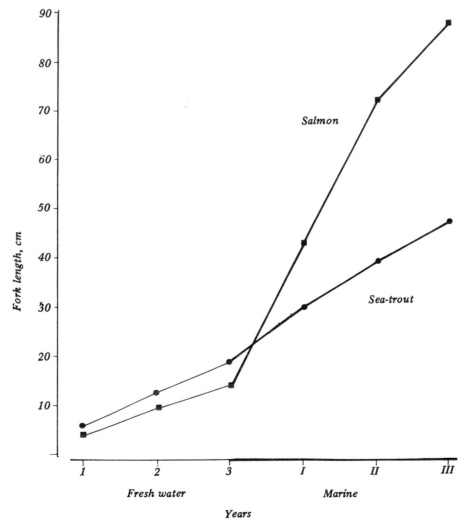

Fig. 27   *The growth of salmon and sea trout from the River Moy.*

Shape

As trout increase in length the skeleton gains flesh but this does not take place at a constant rate. The fish illustrated in Fig. 28 came from the Irish Sea and from an Atlantic feeding trout stock. Their difference in shape is obvious, the fatter trout feeding on a richer diet than the others. The shape of sea trout is far less uniform than their length at any particular age.

Various mathematical ways of dealing with a change in shape have been devised. Scientists who appraise fish stocks and commercial fishermen whose income is determined by the weight of fish they land have an interest in the shape of their quarry. For one thing a trout of a shorter length will be far more acceptable to a buyer if it comes from a rich sea feeding area; a trout of similar length from the Atlantic might not be marketable. But trout shape is of greatest concern to the angler who examines his catch with greater care than any other interested individual.

The invention of *Condition factors* was largely for anglers' use. In simple terms a Condition factor is based on a formula for a particular fish species which relates a series of weights to lengths. The factors are usually derived from an idealised formula which regards the shape of the fish as identical throughout its life or it may be based on some actual example of variation in weight with length in a particular population. From this it can be deduced that there are several Condition factors relating to sea trout. The earliest and most widely applied of these was developed by W.J.M. Menzies and later used by G.H. Nall and other workers. It proposes that the average sea trout would put flesh on its skeleton at the following rates:

Fork length		Weight	
in	*cm*	*lb*	*kg*
7.9	20	0.18	0.08
9.8	25	0.35	0.16
11.8	30	0.59	0.27
13.8	35	0.95	0.43
15.8	40	1.41	0.64
17.7	45	2.00	0.91
19.7	50	2.75	1.25
21.7	55	3.66	1.66
23.6	60	4.76	2.16
25.6	65	6.06	2.75

Fig. 28 Post-smolts from the Atlantic (Currane fishery) (left) and the Irish Sea (right). The Currane fish were captured in fresh water in July 1982; the Irish Sea trout were taken in the sea in May, 1983.

6 in (15 cm)

To apply this test an angler measures the length of his catch and weighs it. He then compares the weight with the ideal one from the Table above. If, for example, his fish is 16 in (40 cm) in length and its weight 1.81 lb (800 g) its Condition factor would be derived by dividing 800 by 640 = 1.25 which is a very well Conditioned trout, 25 per cent heavier than would be expected.

This is acceptable as long as all sea trout conform to the idealised shape envisaged by the developers of the formula. The fact that they do not was the reason for devising others. Nall realised the shortcomings of the factor he himself used so extensively. He recommended that the factor should be fixed a little higher in large and lower in small individuals (0.95 to 0.98 for sea trout of 0.5 to 1 lb (0.23 to 0.45 kg); 1.05 for fish of 3 to 5 lb (1.36 to 2.27 kg) and 1.1 for fish of 6 to 7 lb (2.72 to 3.18 kg)). Obviously that is a cumbersome way of making adjustments.

The more recent approach to the evaluation of Condition would be to work with a large sample of fish from a particular fishery, noting the weight and length of each. The logarithm of the weight would then be correlated with the logarithm of the length and this regression would describe the sample of fish in question. The relationship would be of very transient value, applying only to the sample.

The transient stability and utility of weight and length relationships was recognised by the earliest workers who examined sea trout. They appreciated that Condition factor changed in a stock from one year to the next, from one month to the next and that their weight and length relationship altered as the fish grew. All of which prompts the question of whether there is a standard sea trout shape with which the angler can compare his catch. The Menzies and Nall formula has served over a number of years (it still serves a good number of scientists!) but what reliable information can be drawn from it?

To examine that proposition two weight and length relationships for trout catches from a Donegal (an Atlantic feeding) and an Irish Sea collection of sea trout are set out below for comparison. These are not presented as immutable relationships but rather to illustrate the kind of variation in weight at a particular length which can occur in sea trout. Several points in the Table below are noteworthy. First, the greatest discrepancy between weights at a particular length occurs in the smallest sea-run trout. At 8 in (20 cm) fish from the Irish Sea can be half as heavy again as their equivalents in the Atlantic. Secondly, as the fish in both types of stock grow in length the discrepancy in their weights diminishes.

For both phenomena there are explanations. Richer feeding and more rapid fleshing out of the skeleton are the reason for initially better Condition. As a stock of fish ages its individuals extend in length and each year a greater proportion of them begins to spawn. Once spawning commences it continues annually for as long as each fish lives. There are occasional examples of a missed year in a spawning sequence but these are rare. Spawning is accompanied by a general loss of Condition

| Fork length | | Donegal | | Irish Sea | |
| | | *Weight* | | | |
in	*cm*	*lb*	*kg*	*lb*	*kg*
7.9	20	0.18	0.08	0.29	0.13
9.8	25	0.35	0.16	0.51	0.23
11.8	30	0.62	0.28	0.84	0.38
13.8	35	0.97	0.44	1.23	0.56
15.8	40	1.41	0.64	1.76	0.80
17.7	45	2.00	0.91	2.40	1.09
19.7	50	2.75	1.25	3.15	1.43
21.7	55	3.66	1.66	4.03	1.83
23.6	60	4.76	2.16	5.07	2.30
25.6	65	6.06	2.75	6.23	2.83

and this is never fully regained. The gaunt, kelt-like appearance haunts these mature fish and they approximate to the same shape whether their provenance is the rich feeding of the Irish Sea or a more deprived background in the Atlantic.

Evaluating the Condition factor of fish from either of the two extremes described against the yardstick of the ideal shape conceived by the earlier scientists would confirm the high Condition factors of trout from rich feeding areas and even the relatively poorly Conditioned of these would seem to be exorbitantly fat. Possibly one could get around the problems by devising a second Condition factor to operate for fat fish and the fact that this was not done is a sequel to the concentration of earlier scientific investigations on sea trout in Scotland where slimbodied fish are in the majority. It is not surprising that the most recent approach is to eschew Condition factors altogether.

One final detail remains to be covered here. A number of sea trout stocks which have been described in some detail and accounts of which are in the literature can be classified quite confidently with one of the two growth patterns described in this chapter. Their distribution around the coasts of Britain and Ireland is shown in Fig. 29 from which it will be seen that the more richly feeding stocks occur in greatest numbers in the Irish Sea, legitimising the descriptive terminology applied to them. The majority of poor feeders are distributed along the Atlantic coastline.

KEY

●   *Poor Condition, "Atlantic" growth*

○   *Good Condition, "Irish Sea" growth*

Fig. 29   *The distribution in Britain and Ireland of poorly and*
well Conditioned trout stocks (based on scientific assessments
made over the last fifty years).

7

Return to Freshwater

Having completed a stage of marine growth trout acquire a special interest for fishermen, commercial and sporting. A temporary peak in Condition has been reached and they are at their most lively and the silver livery is at its best. The majority of scientific assessments are based on this stage of the life cycle and angling and commercial catch data refer mostly to it. The artless information dutifully collected by anglers has a value not merely in showing the trends in catch, it also serves to identify the kind of sea trout stock which is being exploited. Just how will now be explained.

Suppose an angler lands two sea trout, one of 8 oz (0.23 kg), the other 5 lb (2.27 kg) in weight. Scrutiny of their scales might reveal the smaller was a post-smolt with the scale formula 2.+ (i.e. of two freshwater years, and a brief sojourn in the sea). The larger might be 3.2+S.M.+ (i.e. three years as a parr in freshwater followed by three sea winters in the last of which the fish spawned). Each of these distinctive combinations of river, pre-spawned sea years and spawning winters constitutes an *age category*. That there is a large range of alternative life strategies available to sea trout, is reflected in the diversity of age categories which might be recorded.

In theory the number of age categories which could be represented in a stock would be a product of the duration of smolt life (in years) multiplied by the maximum sea life of the fish, making allowance for different combinations of virgin and spawning winters. In reality diversity of such a high order is unknown but as many as thirty-five and occasionally forty age categories have been encountered in the course of a routine scale analysis.

The duration of the parr phase has a bearing on the number of age categories contained but the length of sea life exerts a greater influence. This characteristic of the population has a strong influence on all others and it registers in the average weight of angling and certain sorts of net catch.

To illustrate the kind of age analysis undertaken by scientists the composition of two samples from Irish sea trout stocks are set out in Fig. 30. It should be stressed that they are representative of sea trout populations elsewhere in western Europe. Both samples are of

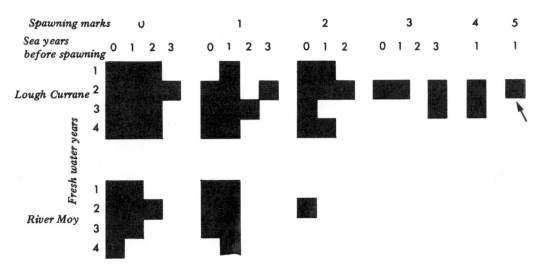

Fig. 30 A simplified diagram showing the age composition of sea trout in two large collections from Lough Currane and the River Moy. Lough Currane fish are long lived; the Moy fish have brief lives.

To obtain the age of any cohort indicated by a square, read off the freshwater age, followed by a full stop, then the number of sea years before spawning and finally the number of spawning marks. The formula for the arrowed square is 2.1 + 5. S.M.

A more detailed account of this Figure is provided in Appendix Table 1.

approximately the same size, about 1,200 fish, and it is important that numbers should be of this high order to minimise distortion and to give a true representative account of the populations.

The Cummeragh sample from Co. Kerry and the Moy sample from Co. Mayo both contain slim-bodied, Atlantic feeding fish. In the Cummeragh there are thirty-seven age categories as against sixteen in the Moy and the Moy trout have only one age category which is not in the other collection (1.S.M.+). The Cummeragh collection on the other hand contains many more of the older sea age categories, particularly of previously spawned fish. Age distributions of these kinds are characteristic of certain populations.

Once a trout descends from freshwater it commences marine growth and puts on weight rapidly at sea. A small proportion of the fish spawns during their first winter following descent, more the next one and the vast majority have commenced spawning by the time they are three sea years of age. As a stock ages, the average weight of an individual in it increases and the probability of its spawning also rises. The growth rates of fish feeding in the same marine area are independent of the age profile of different stocks. Thus, a higher average weight at capture is the result of one stock containing older individuals, being longer lived, than another. And, provided large samples are collected, the percentage of previous spawners which these contain should correlate with the average weight according to one of the relationships described for

British and Irish sea trout. Knowing whether the samples came from a rich, Irish Sea feeding stock or a poorly Conditioned Atlantic feeding stock is essential.

Average weight		Percentage previous spawners	
lb	*kg*	*Irish Sea growth*	*Atlantic growth*
1.0	0.5	14	15
1.5	0.7	20	28
2.0	0.9	26	42
3.0	1.4	42	69
4.0	1.8	54	86

Some variations are likely to occur in the records of weights from the same fishery over a number of years but the overall average should enable a classification of the stock concerned. The long-lived stocks are extremely valuable particularly from the sporting point of view. Stocks which have been assessed and classified to date are shown in Fig. 31 from which it will be seen that long-lived sea trout are not very common and that they are concentrated on the western coasts of Britain and Ireland.

One caveat about the above Table must be stressed: it applies only to sea trout around the coasts of Britain and Ireland. That there are various degrees of large size among sea trout is appreciated. Vistula sea trout have been described as very large, comparable with salmon. A range of 28 to 40 in (70 to 100 cm) has been given for a sample of trout from the Dunajec River. In age they ranged between four and six years. Even in the case of the Ailort (a long-lived Scottish stock), fish of between 28 and 32 in (70 and 80 cm) fork length were a mere 0.4 per cent of the sample examined. 'Large' sea trout in Scotland are smaller than 'large' Polish fish.

Between the long-lived sea trout stocks of Ireland and Scotland there is considerable similarity, both in their age structure and the crude statistics describing their exploitation. For instance W.A. Adamson in an account of sea trout catches in Loch Lomond between 1949 and 1958 inclusive, gave the average annual mean weight at capture within the extremes of 1.9 to 3 lb (0.86 to 1.34 kg); average weights at capture of 1.8 lb (0.82 kg) have been given for Currane sea trout between 1974 and 1976; in 1975 the figure was 2.0 lb (0.91 kg).

Only a part of the sea trout stock comes into freshwater and the brackish water of river mouths. Throughout the year there are always some trout in the sea and it is only the spawning (usually older) fish which *must* make an appearance in freshwater. Younger trout have an

KEY

●   *Long lived stock*

✪   *Short lived stock*

Fig. 31   Classification of British and Irish sea trout stocks as long or short-lived according to technical accounts of the fish.

option of staying in marine conditions during the winter or moving into freshwater. If they choose the alternative of joining the freshwater ingress they may or may not spawn. The alternatives open to a post-smolt during its first post-migration winter are shown diagramatically in Fig. 32. At one extreme the entire winter may be passed in the sea; at the other the fish return to freshwater after a short excursion to tidal waters and pass the winter months there, spawning or not. An intermediate scenario would see the trout successively in the sea, river, estuary, river and sea within the space of ten months.

Salmon re-enter freshwater for the purpose of spawning although that need not take place for as much as a year later in the case of

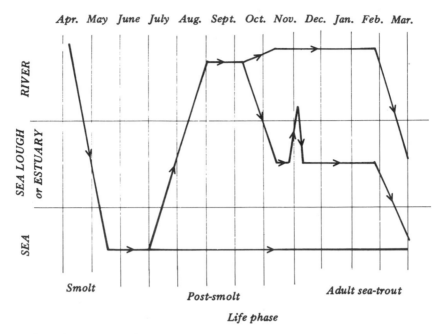

Apr. May June July Aug. Sept. Oct. Nov. Dec. Jan. Feb. Mar.

RIVER

SEA LOUGH or ESTUARY

SEA

Smolt

Post-smolt

Adult sea-trout

Life phase

Fig. 32   Options of a sea trout in the year following its first descent from freshwater.

spring fish. But for sea trout the migration is not always a spawning one. However it is not altogether divorced from spawning either. As a sea trout ages its proximity to spawning increases and its movements into freshwater become more purposeful and specific. In the early excursions, any freshwater body will do. Later the natal river and finally even the redd from which the fish emerged may be sought out. Older trout would be expected to run into freshwater in larger numbers than younger ones. A higher proportion of older than younger smolts returns to freshwater during the summer of their first descent. This can benefit fisheries exploiting sea trout because a low mean smolt age is associated with larger numbers of the fish and a higher mean smolt age with a smaller exodus of juveniles. More of the larger older juveniles will first revisit freshwater in their first year of migration, fewer of the younger, smaller smolts, and this tends towards a fairly steady level of exploitable stock, provided post-smolts are captured and retained.

There are other factors which militate in favour of a stable exploitable sea trout stock. Both have been introduced already. Their technical descriptions are *divided migration* and *return*. Divided migration simply means that the progeny of a certain sea trout spawning year will not all go to sea at once; a tiny number will do so after their first freshwater winter, the majority after their second year, a smaller proportion after three and the remainder after four years. And then, these fish, once in the sea, will make a divided return to freshwater, in instalments rather than all together. This contrasts with, for example, grilse fisheries where the majority of smolts go seawards after two years and return one sea winter later. As many as 80 per cent of the grilse in Irish fisheries observe this migration pattern. As a result the grilse fishing in any one year depends to a large extent on the numbers of broodstock three years earlier. Fluctuations of this kind are far less extreme in sea trout, the variability of whose good and poor years are smoothed out by the divided nature of migration and return.

Their ambivalence in re-entering freshwater and the vast array of age categories which are represented in a population would suggest that trout mix together in freshwater in a fairly haphazard way, and it is true that angling for sea trout will yield an array of age groups if the angling effort is concentrated on, say, a large freshwater lake. But the netsman or angler situated on a river just above the tide, provided water levels are adequate to sustain an invasion of the fish, will see a definite sequence of re-entry, to which the majority conform. All trout migrations in and out of freshwater are summarised diagramatically in Fig. 33. The largest fish (the older virgins and previous spawners (mended kelts)) make their appearance first, from about March onwards. This biological adaptation reduces competition between these and the later descent of smolts to the tide. The end result can be seen in angling statistics which, if they are analysed at monthly intervals, will show a decline in the average weight of catch from the spring. It follows that where the trout stock is short-lived very few if any will re-enter the river in spring. Where there are good numbers of longer-lived trout they constitute a recognisable spring run which is distinctive and an unerring indication of the occurrence of a long-lived stock.

Sea trout that spawn

Older sea trout are more likely to be spawners. Maturity is therefore connected with age, or size or both. When post-smolts have been held in captivity approximately 25 per cent of them spawned the following winter. The percentage of post-smolts which spawns is variable. Judged from the numbers of adult sea trout of one sea winter to bear spawning marks the percentage has fluctuated between less than 1 and 60 per cent in Britain and Ireland. Assessments carried out on sea trout stocks from the Welsh side of the Irish Sea (although few in number) suggest that the percentage of post-smolts to spawn there is much higher than among Atlantic feeding sea trout. An average of about 10 per cent of the latter would spawn first as post-smolts but among the richer feeding fish the average would be in the vicinity of 30 per cent.

The quality of feeding also influences the number of eggs produced. A female from rich Irish Sea feeding conditions of 20 in (50 cm) fork length would contain about 2,700 eggs but a fish of the same length

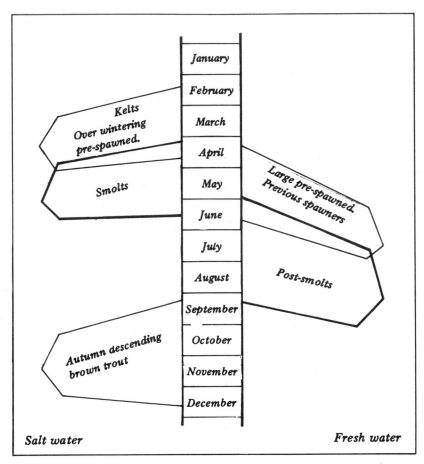

Fig. 33 Migrations of sea trout of different ages and reproductive status.

from Atlantic surroundings would yield only slightly more than 2,000 or only about 75 per cent of its more richly fed equivalent.

If the Condition of sea trout exerts an influence on the percentage of post-smolts to spawn the next question is whether the life expectancy of a stock modifies its spawning behaviour. The evidence implies that it does, that short-lived fish tend to mature slightly earlier. Which is just as well because short-lived stocks survive far too briefly to produce a large number of previous spawners. A slightly earlier maturation may be an adaptive means of ensuring that enough eggs are laid.

To generalise about British and Irish sea trout, a proportion would spawn first as post-smolts and the majority by the following year. Examination of the scales of previously spawned fish indicates their average age at first spawning to be between 1.5 and 2.5 sea years. In other words, the majority of fish commence spawning in their second 'sea' or post-migration winter.

The chosen ground

Trout and salmon lay their eggs in gravel excavations (redds) prepared by the female which, after spawning, covers them over by fanning movements of the caudal fin. The gravel grades must not be too large in relation to the fish which cannot generate sufficient power to shift large rocks. Nor should they be too fine. A circulation of water bringing oxygen to the eggs is essential and silt suffocates them.

Various statements have been made describing ideal circumstances for salmonid spawning but a close investigation of brown trout suggests that they are not too fussy about exactly where they place redds in pools or riffles. The spawning gravels are not well sorted and there is little redd structure. Nor can the redd mount (the pile of stones left by the female) have much functional significance because it is quickly flattened by the first spate. Brown trout are not wary of silt accumulations either, although it is possible that much of the finer grades are displaced downstream while the redd is being dug.

The materials used in redd construction are distributed among three main grades: sands with a maximum particle dimension of 2 mm, gravels whose maximum particle dimension extends to 3.2 cm and, above this, debris and boulders. Of these, gravels constitute the bulk of redd material; in twenty-four Irish Atlantic salmon redds, sampled for comparison, more than 75 per cent of the grades were gravels. Salmon redds differ from those of sea trout in that they occasionally include some small boulders. Presumably fragments of this size are too large to be moved by sea trout. Apart from this the materials used by salmon and trout in redd construction have much in common and it is probable that small grilse and large sea trout would select a similar substratum in which to deposit their eggs.

In other respects also sea trout overlap in their spawning with other forms of their species and with salmon. Trout are supposed to penetrate further upstream into shallower water than could accommodate the larger species but this is not a completely effective segregation mechanism either. And although most trout spawn approximately a month before the majority of salmon the two species frequently coincide on the redds and salmon-trout hybrids often occur in the wild.

Of the several barriers devised by nature to keep spawning trout and salmon apart, timing is perhaps the most effective. Trout spawn in October and November and salmon in November and December. These two periods overlap and in the month of November it would be quite usual to find trout and salmon mingling in the same pools waiting to move onto the redds.

Within the species *Salmo trutta* interbreeding of resident and sea-run forms is assumed to occur and the precise role of precocious male parr is not fully understood. The occurrence of spawning resident brown trout in close proximity to the sea-run form maximises the possibility of both participating in a successful fertilisation when either is represented by few individuals. Faced with a selection of these trout it can be difficult to recognise which is a resident brown. Sea-run trout will display signs of sea-feeding on the scales so that their identification is straightforward enough. Spawning females without signs of marine growth can probably be described as resident trout. These fish will certainly be smaller than sea trout of the same age. Comparative average lengths at age for brown and sea trout sampled on the redds in Connemara in 1981 illustrate this point. The age is a total figure combining, in the case of the sea-run fish, the parr and marine years.

Age	'Resident'		Fork lengths	Sea-run	
	in	*cm*		*in*	*cm*
3	10.6	27.0		12.7	32.2
4	11.1	28.2		15.2	38.6
5	12.1	30.7		18.9	48.0
6				20.1	51.1
7				22.2	56.4
8				25.2	64.0

Among salmonids the female digs a redd and the male fertilises her eggs as they are discharged into the gravel excavation. The female then fans the gravels back over the eggs affording them protection until they hatch. One large cock fish will fertilise a hen fish and the small mature male, parr have a covert role, scurrying in over the eggs at the last crucial moment. Large cock fish fight to keep one another off the redds and they also resent the presence of the small intruders. These behavioural features are very likely common to the majority if not all strains of trout.

Within the two types of genetically distinctive sea trout, in Ireland described respectively as long- and short-lived, two very different kinds of spawning tactics are displayed. These are very likely to occur in similar kinds of fish inhabiting Scotland and Wales and the behaviour concerned could provide a partial explanation for the occurrence of these stocks, but this will be returned to later.

In the Currane fishery which is on the Cummeragh system in Co. Kerry and has the only known long-lived sea trout population in Ireland, the fish spawn regularly in early November; the precise time may alter depending on local weather and climatic considerations. The bulk of spawning activity is crammed into a single week. At that time the usual array of trout forms, resident, sea-run and precocious will present themselves on the redds. A detailed assessment of these spawning congregations was undertaken in 1980. Females out-numbered males at all places in the river system up to about 6 miles (10 km) above the tide, occasionally by two to one. Males were most abundant within close reach of the sea, suggesting they were not very mobile and preferred a shorter migration.

The following spawning season a similar investigation was undertaken in Connemara where the sea trout stocks are of the short-lived kind. This census of breeding fish was supplemented by hatchery records collected in the course of artificial propagation.

For Connemara sea trout the spawning period is a protracted one. The behaviour of the fish is analogous to that of the mosquito. The males of that insect combine in mating swarms of many thousands of individuals; so dense is the appearance of the flies that the swarms are visible for some distance; the females locate and visit them in ones and twos. The density of male sea trout in the short-lived stocks is nothing so spectacular but they are persistent, waiting on and around the redds over a long period to be visited by the occasional female. It is a form of behaviour which holds considerable potential; always being there, ever prepared to fertilise whatever female appears. It is an insidious tactic and it may well be the explanation for the success and widespread occurrence of short-lived stocks of sea trout and the infrequency of long-lived fish.

8

And Creatures Great and Small

No man is an island, trout are even less alone whether in the open upper layers of the sea or the teeming streams and lakes of their parr life. Most relationships with other organisms are perilous, potentially lethal. From their earliest days they are in competition with their fellows for food and space, wisely avoiding the larger members of their own species. Contacts with smaller forms of life are summary and fatal for the smaller form, and they vie with other fish species for animal prey.

This part of the picture we have briefly seen. The rest is the panoply of creatures which depend to some extent on sea trout. In strictly mechanistic terms sea trout, however highly they are rated by fishermen, are merely a part of a food chain. But it is from the fisherman's point of view that the animals which leave their marks on sea trout are reviewed. Correctly interpreted the marks have a tale to tell. And some of the organisms feeding literally on and in the fish are a vital clue to its immediate history. We are then considering a brief list of common sea trout parasites and predators. A more comprehensive account of the role played by sea trout in the food chains of river and sea is not possible; too little is known about their place in the hierarchy.

Some internal parasites

The list of parasite species occurring in the alimentary system of sea trout includes five whose abundance can be related to the feeding activity of their host. Four of these belong to the Phylum Platyhelminthes (Flatworms) and three of those are digenetic trematodes, small leaf-like worms each equipped with two suckers which they use to move around the host. The flatworms which measure up to and occasionally exceed 0.1 in (3 mm) glide among the debris of the fishbones, scales and chitinous skeletons of invertebrates in the gut. The larger are visible to the naked eye and may be recognised by their shape. Do not be too concerned about the technical terminology used to describe them or the details to which reference is made in making an identification. Going further into the meaning of the terminology is beyond the scope of this work.

Within the Digenea there is considerable variation in the shape of the body and the arrangement of the internal organs. They possess a digestive system and the three species which concern us here are all hermaphrodite; the shape and disposition of certain of the reproductive organs is distinctive and should be recognisable at a magnification of about X20 so that while the organisms survive — which they may for up to forty-eight hours after the death of the trout, depending on the conditions in which the fish has been stored — it should be possible to search the gut contents for them. The following notes and Fig. 34 may be used to separate the trematodes but these observations will not suffice to distinguish between them and closely related species with which they may co-exist.

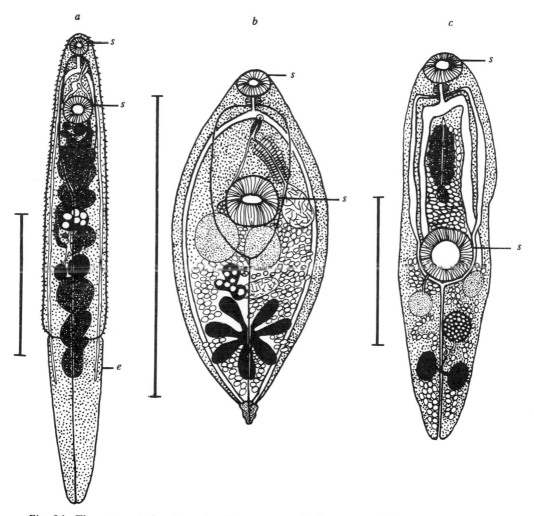

Fig. 34 Three trematodes from the alimentary canal of sea trout: (a) Hemiurus communis, *(b)* Lecithaster gibbosus *and (c)* Derogenes varicus, *(e) ecsoma and (s) sucker. Scale lines all represent 1mm.*

Hemiurus communis

This flatworm is the most narrowly-shaped of the three species although much of its length is to be found in the tail-like ecsoma which can be retracted into the main body or soma. *Hemiurus* differs from the other two in having an ecsoma; its two suckers are close together at the anterior end of the body. *H. communis* is invariably found in the stomach although specimens have occasionally been recovered from the pyloric region of the sea trout gut. When the stomach is ridged and contracted locating and counting these organisms can be a tedious operation.

Lecithaster gibbosus

Lecithaster is the smallest of the three flatworms and most leaf-like in shape. The suckers are further separated than in *Hemiurus*. *Lecithaster* is largely confined to the intestine although occasional specimens are found in the pyloric area. This species has been taken in large numbers in sea trout from the Irish Sea though not on the Atlantic coast.

Derogenes varicus

Derogenes is elongate, broader than *Hemiurus* but narrower than *Lecithaster*. The posterior sucker is closer to the centre of the body than in either of the other trematodes. The stronghold of *Derogenes* is said to be the stomach but it is an active species which makes rapid *post mortem* migrations to other parts of the alimentary canal.

The life cycle of the trematodes is very complex, involving several hosts in each of which the organism assumes a different form. The eggs develop in the final host (a fish though not necessarily a trout) from which they are voided with the faeces; an early larval stage develops in an invertebrate intermediate host — thought to be a copepod for at least one of the three described above (*Hemiurus*). Fish are probably infected through consuming small planktonic forms such as copepods, but the fodder species such as sand eels and sprats are more likely to pick up the parasites by this route than sea trout, which select larger prey. Parasites which are concentrated by fodder fish can survive in the gut of later predators and this is thought to be the mechanism by which sea trout, feeding largely on fish, as for example in the Irish Sea, accumulate large numbers of worms. Along the Atlantic coast these parasites would seem to be less plentiful.

Several biological processes contribute to the numbers of Digenea in the alimentary canal of a sea trout. Any of the three species listed may be absent in specific circumstances, possibly because they do not occur in the geographical area concerned. As with most species which have an annual life cycle there are months in which they may be abundant followed by others in which they are less frequent. Superimposed on this is the feeding behaviour of the host which consumes the fodder fish in which the Digenea are already established, and accumulates the parasites while it actively feeds. Sea trout are believed to glut feed so that numbers of the worms will build up rapidly and be lost very quickly once feeding slows down and the fish move into freshwater. In these circumstances the trout will accumulate a further parasite burden when it resumes marine feeding later.

The interaction of various biological factors makes accurate prediction of the digenean parasite burden of an individual sea trout difficult but large sea trout would be expected to contain more Digenea than small. For fish of comparable size, an Atlantic feeding stock which has a diet containing a small proportion of fish would contain fewer parasites than would be accumulated by sea trout in richer feeding conditions. In either case the parasites would be more abundant in the summer months, the numbers declining in the autumn and winter and rising again in the spring.

Eubothrium crassum

Eubothrium crassum (Fig. 35) belongs to another group of flatworms, the Cestoda or tapeworms whose bodies are long and segmented. At the anterior end is the head or *scolex* which anchors the worm in the host. The segmented body hangs in the gut and, as the segments mature, they drop off and are voided to the outside world. As is the case for many parasite species *Eubothrium* uses an intermediate host, probably a copepod before completing its life cycle in a fish. *E. crassum* is a large parasite, unlike the digeneans already described. It has a ribbon shape at any length between 0.1 in and 12 in (3 mm to 30 cm). The worm makes its initial appearance in a host fish as a small egg shaped blob of tissue which grows into a segmented tape. Slicing open the pyloric region, just behind the stomach of an infected salmonid, the large cream-coloured *Eubothrium* spill out. Like the digenean flatworms however the incidence of infection by *Eubothrium* can be related to the abundance of suitable sea trout fodder organisms and the worm is far more abundant in the Irish Sea than on the Atlantic coast. Virtually all trout in the Irish Sea, from post-smolts to fish of five sea winters contain small numbers. In a sea lough in Co. Donegal 75 per cent of two sea winter fish contained the worm. While these levels of infection are not very different from those in the Irish Sea the size of the worm burden (i.e. total number per infected fish) varied a lot. In the Atlantic sea lough the number of *Eubothrium* per infected fish was ten times less than in the Irish Sea.

Care must be taken in making comparisons of levels of infection because as for the digenean flatworms, there is a seasonal build-up and decline in *Eubothrium* which achieves its maximum numbers following

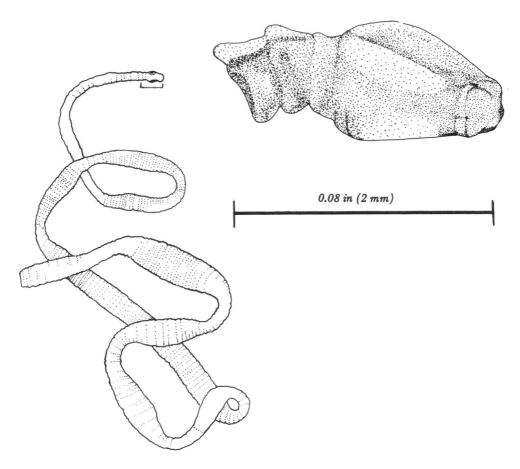

0.08 in (2 mm)

Fig. 35 Mature Eubothrium crassum *from the pyloric region of a sea trout gut; scolex enlarged.*

summer feeding by the trout. The largest numbers of *Eubothrium* occur in trout from the Irish Sea (or rich feeding) and these are numerous enough to allow one to describe the worm burden in each age group of sea trout. Only very small ribbon-shaped individuals occur in post-smolts, suggesting that the worm originates as a marine infection. On this point there has been some controversy and it is possible that two marine and a freshwater race of the tapeworm contribute to the final burden. Trout of one sea winter contain two length groups of worms in the summer months, corresponding to the most recent infection (which is similar to that in post-smolts) and an older age group. Trout of two sea winters contain three length groups of *Eubothrium*. Thus there are indications that *Eubothrium* continues its growth for two years after entering its host.

As long as the host remains in the sea and does not undertake the change of medium which a migration to freshwater entails, or the physiological stress of starvation at spawning time, the cestode probably continues its development. Once spawning begins, and contrary to the situation which has been described for *Eubothrium* in freshwater races of salmonids, the worms are lost so there is a reduction rather than an increase in *Eubothrium* numbers, as sea trout age and grow.

Like the digenean flatworms *Eubothrium* could be used as an indicator of feeding conditions. It might also be used to corroborate details of the life cycle of its host. Where there are large enough numbers of this parasite their lengths might be used to estimate sea age of the trout in which they are found.

Thynnascaris adunca

The nematode or roundworm *Thynnascaris* occurs commonly in inshore fish and is the most abundant roundworm species occurring in sea trout which consume it along with the sprats and sand eels which contribute to the food chain. Numbers of *Thynnascaris* reach a maximum at the time of most intensive feeding by the trout but, once this slows down, they are rapidly lost. Two stages of the worm are distinguishable under magnification (Fig. 36). The tail of the stage iii terminates in a small cuticular hook while in the stage iv this is replaced by a small thorny 'cactus tail'. Both stages may grow within the trout host. As with the other parasites the incidence of infection and the burden of *Thynnascaris* are greatly influenced by the feeding conditions of the trout and particularly by the amount of fish in the diet. A burden of as many as 300 per infected trout in the Irish Sea is common whereas in the Atlantic more than five per infected trout is unusual, although there may be local exceptions to these numbers.

To summarise, all of the parasites which occur commonly in the sea trout gut are found in other fish also. Their life cycles are complex and in addition to a fish host they require an invertebrate — probably a crustacean. The majority are likely to enter the sea trout when already established in the fodder fish on which the trout prey. Large numbers of these gut parasites are therefore a sign that the trout fed to a large extent on fish prey and that in turn suggests feeding of the Irish Sea kind.

The number of gut parasites, relative to the amount of food in the stomach, could be an indicator of the physiological state of the fish. A large number of parasites, an empty stomach and food remains in the intestine would suggest that sea feeding has ceased and that a fish was about to or had already entered freshwater. Conversely, a full stomach, particularly if the food is of fish remains, an empty intestine, and few parasites would suggest that the fish recently left fresh water.

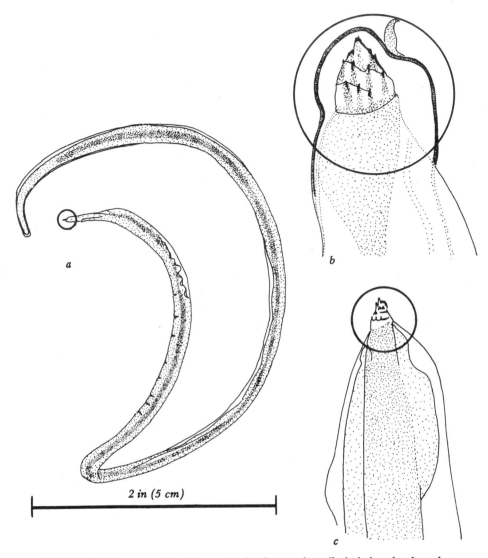

Fig. 36 (a) The nematode Thynnascaris adunca, *the tail circled and enlarged as (b) showing a late stage iii, the 'cactus tail' visible through the cuticle which has a cuticular hook and (c) a stage iv, the 'cactus tail' fully exposed.*

An external parasite

Lepeophtheirus salmonis

Sea lice belong to a morphologically highly variable group, the copepods. The parasite *Lepeophtheirus* (Fig. 37) infects only salmonids and occurs only in the sea. Because it does not survive long in fresh water its presence there can be regarded as a sign that its host has recently left salt water.

The sea louse has ten stages in its life cycle, the first three of which,

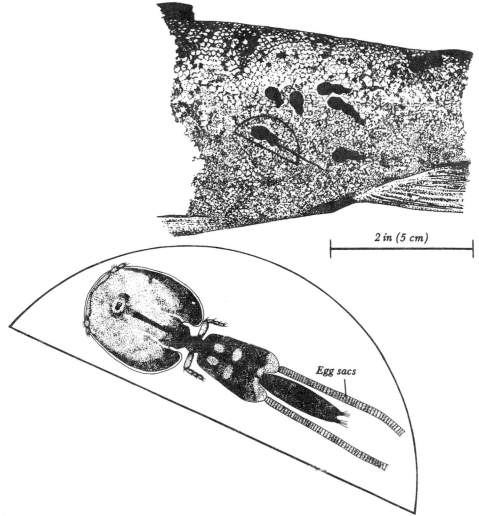

2 in (5 cm)

Egg sacs

Fig. 37 The copepod sea louse Lepeophtheirus salmonis *clustered on a sea trout and (enlarged) a female.*

after the egg, are passed in the plankton. The fourth attaches itself to the salmonid skin. By the eighth stage the sexes are distinguishable and from then on the lice are attached to their host by suction. The eggs are stored in two trailing egg sacs on the female louse where they hatch. Once the salmonid enters fresh water the egg sacs fall off so their presence, before the louse later parts company with its host, is a sign that the fish very recently left the sea.

Completion of the life cycle and reproduction of sea lice can take place all the year round but there is a general slowing down in the winter months. The occurrence of the parasite reflects this and from June to October they tend to be more abundant than during the remainder of the year. The pattern of infection on sea trout may differ slightly from that on salmon which can mount an inflammatory response to the copepods. Salmon are least capable of this in spring and autumn at which times their infestation by sea lice is greatest.

Close encounters of a largely indeterminate kind

Sea trout and salmon, in the course of a dangerous life cycle, evade a variety of predators and undertake hazardous and arduous migrations. Inevitably near misses inflict scars and marks whose interpretation could serve to identify a particular kind and source of predation.

The angler who handles fewer fish than the commercial fisherman and examines each individual more carefully is probably more sensitive to imperfections on the carcass. Sidney Spencer claimed:

> Fish with unhealed wounds from seal or otter bites or from accidental damage sustained at river obstacles are common and in a group of fish will always be the first to take.

And the same author wrote:

> Prompting interest in the entire question was and is the fact that injured fish are readiest to take. I personally find that on days of poor conditions when fish are 'off' so that one records one fish for the day — that single fish often bears an injury.

Of all the angling writers Sidney Spencer has provided the most comprehensive account of scars and marks to date; reference will be made to it in the course of this chapter. The main perpetrators of scars and marks are listed blow.

Fish: Male sea trout are known to be aggressive to one another at spawning time and adults attack and mark precocious parr with a characteristic scar of two parallel lines. It is however thought unlikely that this persists in the adult fish. Just how long any scar or mark remains visible is unknown and complicates the identification of its cause.

The most characteristic scar inflicted by a fish is that of the sea lamprey *Petromyzon marinus*. When the Welland Canal circumvented Niagara Falls it provided access to the Great Lakes for this anadromous species whose depredations on a range of fish species there have provoked much research into its biology.

The sea lamprey spends four to five years in freshwater before going to sea where it attains a length of 30 in (75 cm) before returning to spawn. In the sea it remains close inshore, within a depth of 137 fathoms (300m) between latitudes 30° and 53° North. Lampreys have acute vision and strong swimming ability and host species are not frightened by them. Attacks can take place all over the body but in vulnerable areas, such as the belly, they are likely to prove fatal. For this reason there is a higher recorded incidence of wounds on the backs of surviving hosts.

The suction exerted by a feeding lamprey is so powerful that it may cause an indentation on the opposite side of a fish 1 to 2 in (3 to 5 cm) in width. Fig. 38 shows a healing lamprey attack mark. The central part of the wound is exposed flesh. This is surrounded by white necrotic skin suggesting by its size that the lamprey moved about on the wound.

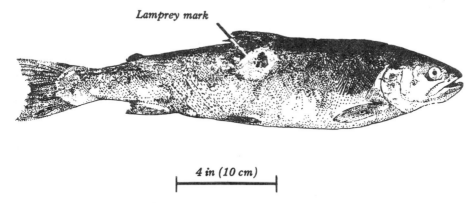

Lamprey mark

4 in (10 cm)

Fig. 38   One sea-winter sea trout bearing a lamprey attack mark.

Mammals: A long list of British mammals known to inflict damage on fish has been provided and one authority identified the water shrew *Neomys fodiens* as the most destructive. Its damage is however directed at the early juvenile stages and, as with the marks made by adult male sea trout on precocious parr, any injuries it dispenses are unlikely to be recognised at a later stage in the life history.

Both grey and common seals are known to consume salmon and sea trout. Signs of seal damage on salmon include missing chunks of flesh and tooth and claw marks but many of the fish on which this damage has been reported were observed as mutilated fragments in fishermen's nets. It is doubtful whether a sea trout of average catch size would survive a seal encounter or be sufficiently large to display the tooth or claw marks following an attack.

The common porpoise *Phocaena phocaena* has been reported as a predator of salmon. In fact, cod, herring, sprat and transparent goby were the fish species most commonly consumed by porpoises in the Baltic where neither salmon nor sea trout was included. Elsewhere it has been concluded that nothing as large as a salmon could feature in the porpoise diet and that most of the food items were less than 10 in (25 cm) long. However herring, sprat and sand eel, species with which sea trout are associated and with which post-smolt sea trout might be consumed, have been listed among its stomach contents.

Mammals, whose jaws are sufficiently small to leave an imprint on the flesh of sea trout, include the otter and mink. Their dentition is very similar (Fig. 39) but the otter skull can be twice as large as that of mink. Spencer described otter marks as:

> Small radius 'half moon' wounds on salmon — too narrow to be seal bites. To the rear of the dorsal fin; often just above the wrist of the tail. Look for all the world as though the pursuer had grabbed and all but missed contact.

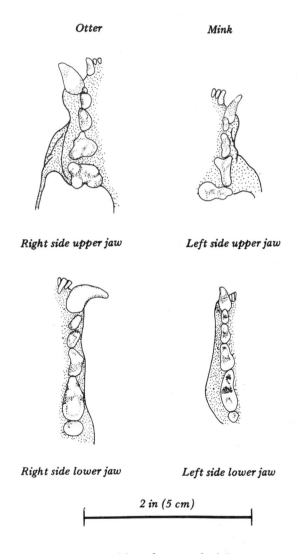

Fig. 39 Dentition of otter and mink.

Birds: Approximately fifty to sixty species of British birds are known to destroy freshwater fish. Some take the eggs and early juveniles and others make inroads on the parr and smolts of salmonids. Although relatively few are suspected of regularly attacking trout of sea-run dimensions three are known to do so. Spencer wrote of the cormorant:

> (when) . . . the dark arch villain strikes and misses the evidence does not long remain since it usually consists of rough slashes of displaced scales on both sides of the escaping fish but these marks are not uncommonly seen in fresh finnock and small sea trout. There may also be damaged tails and torn fins from the same cause.

A review of the feeding of divers, grebes, mergansers and auks in Denmark, identified the cormorant as the most consistent predator of fish larger than 15 in (38 cm). Work carried out in Ireland described the food of cormorants in inshore waters; wrasse of 4 to 14 in (10 to 36 cm), eels of 26 in (66 cm) and flat fish up to 8 in (20 cm) long were consumed; the dimensions suggest that a cormorant could cope with a sea trout of one sea winter. In Scotland brown trout of 2.4 lb (1.1 kg) have been reported from a cormorant stomach.

Herons have long been perceived as competitors with man for freshwater fish. They are reported of being capable of consuming a trout of up to 3 lb (1.4 kg) in weight.

The third significant piscivorous bird species is the gannet which occurs around the British and Irish coasts with major colonies off southwest Ireland (Little Skellig, 10,000 to 20,000 pairs; Bull Rock 1,000 to 1,500 pairs). Sea trout caught in the Currane fishery in Co. Kerry are fairly heavily 'slashed' and 'punctured' and, as gannets abound in its vicinity, they are prime suspects. One scientist has reported:

> A gannet can swallow four large mackerel in succession, ten herrings or a codling 18 in (46 cm) long and thicker than a man's forearm at the head.

So a two winter sea trout would seem to be within its capabilities. The distribution of gannets is linked with that of herring, mackerel and sprats and the association of sea trout with juvenile herrings and sprats has been referred to. Gannets feed by taking their prey from below and swallowing small fish under water. Larger prey are taken to the surface and shaken and there are records of exceptionally large fish being speared.

Attempts to relate specific scars to these three bird predators were made by preparing detailed studies of their skulls (Fig. 40). This approach has been successfully used in North American investigations to distinguish between the scars made by the blue heron and the belted kingfisher on the size and shape of the bill mark but heron, cormorant and gannet are capable of injuring a fish in an identical way although

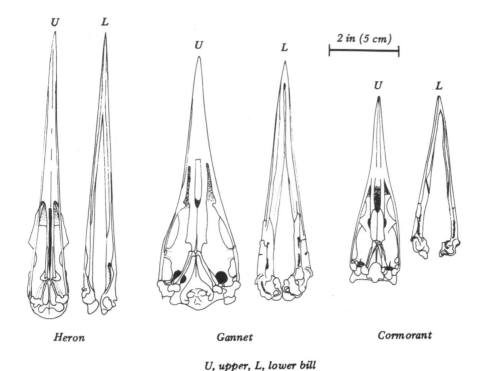

Heron   Gannet   Cormorant

U, upper, L, lower bill

Fig. 40   Skulls of heron, gannet and cormorant.

it is likely that the fish illustrated in Fig. 41 was damaged by a swimming bird which approached it from below rather than, say, by a heron.

Once a predatory bird has made contact with a relatively large fish it must bring it to the surface before swallowing it and, while

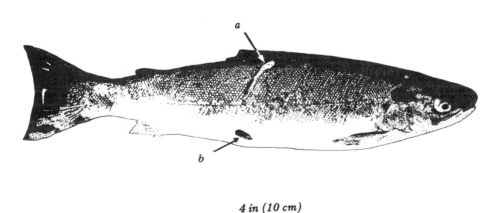

Fig. 41   Post-smolt sea trout bearing marks of 'cormorant attack':
(a) slash and (b) stab or puncture.

the prey is being re-oriented in the bill, it can escape. Subsequent attempts at recapture may result in additional wounds. Thus it is likely that the fish presented in Fig. 42 made its escape from a cormorant which was able to renew the chase from the surface rather than a gannet which first would need to become airborne again.

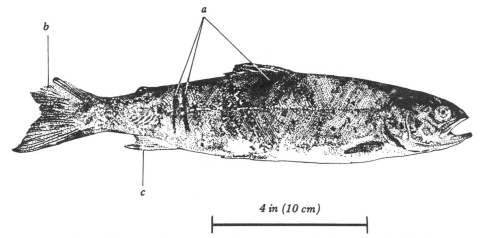

Fig. 42 *Post-smolt sea trout showing the probable marks of a bird attack: (a) scale removal; (b) torn caudal fin and (c) skin removal exposing musculature.*

Net mesh marks: Fishing nets can be classified as belonging to two main groups: *enclosing* or *meshing*. Fish do not interact with enclosing gear (a landing net would be an example) but are simply retained by it. Meshing or gill nets (of which drift nets are an example) operate by 'gilling' the fish which jams in a single mesh. The mechanism can be envisaged by regarding the anterior end of the fish as a cone which, in the case of salmonids, has its base or widest part in the vicinity of the anterior end of the dorsal fin. If the mesh perimeter exceeds the widest circumference of the fish it will not be constrained whereas if the mesh is smaller than the head it will not admit the fish. These are the extremes; gill nets are selective however and grip most effectively where the maximum girth of the fish exceeds the mesh by 25 per cent.

The typical mark left by a meshing net is an area of scale removal and a cut or scar around the fish within the meshing zone (Fig. 43). Once the fish has jammed in a mesh its struggles may result in further scale removal and scarring on other parts of the body. It is doubtful whether many such fish escape to be captured by other means subsequently. The typical marks on the anterior part of the body are a necessary indication that meshing occurred.

Another kind of enmeshment takes place when a salmonid strikes a

Fig. 43   Post-smolt with a 'gilling' mesh mark (arrowed).

net whose mesh size is small in relation the fish's body and whose thread is very fine. First contact is possibly by the teeth of the salmonid becoming entangled so that the body rolls into the netting and the fins are pinned. Extensive scale removal is likely to occur although the chances of the fish escaping to be captured elsewhere are minimal.

The expansion of drift netting for salmon in recent years has resulted in a greater frequency of net mesh marks on incoming salmonids. The incidence of these marks on Atlantic salmon and sea trout was reported in Norwegian waters in 1979. The net mark frequency varied with the size of the fish and its incidence was much higher on grilse than salmon because they, being smaller, had a greater chance of passing through the net and escaping with a typical small net mark on the dorsal fin. However mesh marks were fewer on sea trout (7.2 per cent marked) than on grilse of comparable size (79.1 per cent marked). A similar situation prevails in Irish waters where the Salmon Research Trust of Ireland reported that in 1981 32.3 per cent of incoming salmon in June, 22.5 per cent in July, 11.8 per cent in August and 18.2 per cent in September were mesh marked. Only 2.2 per cent of the total sea trout run (24 of 1,110 fish) were similarly mutilated.

Marks on spawning trout: Spawning sea trout are known to attack precocious male parr. In the vicinity of the redds males have been observed nipping one another and thus displacing rivals. To what extent these activities leave marks is not known.

For female rainbow trout spawning has been reported as arduous:

> . . . the female's tail may become worn and frayed from digging and her body bruised and scratched . . .

Males do not assist with redd excavation.

Two distinctive spawning strategies have been described for sea trout from the Waterville fishery (the Cummeragh system) and the Connemara region. In the Cummeragh the fish congregate at high densities for a relatively short period and undertake intensive spawning activity. In Connemara the males wait on the redds for a long period and the females visit them in small numbers. A proportion of the trout in both stocks was marked at the following incidence (expressed as marks per 100 fish):

	Cummeragh	Connemara
Males	10	16
Females	20	17

The actual form of mark could not be attributed with certainty to any cause but they could have been inflicted by birds (Fig. 44). In this connection the protracted stay of males on the redds in Connemara, exposing them to bird attack over a longer period, may be the explanation.

Fig. 44 Composite diagram illustrating marks and scars on 103 male sea trout examined on the redds in Connemara in 1981.

Interpreting the scars, marks and wounds of sea-run trout is an uncertain chore, providing much grist for speculation. And, while the possible or even probable causes of injury are known, being categorical about their identity is fraught with danger. In 1982 circulars requesting details of lesions on rod-caught salmonids were circulated to fishermen in Ireland. Twenty replies describing sea trout and twenty referring to salmon were received.

On salmon the majority of injuries occurred in the meshing zone, at the anterior end of the body. The average weight of these fish was one-third lower than the national catch from draft and drift nets and was consistent with a fish of smaller size squeezing through a mesh just too large to grip it. The majority of scars on sea trout on the other hand, could be described as 'bird marks'. The average weight of these fish was fairly close to that of the average rod catch for the year.

There are no completely satisfactory methods of identifying the causes of marks and scars on sea trout and salmon but the angler's instinct expressed by Sidney Spencer in 1969 contained probably more than a grain of truth:

> It is widely believed in the fishing circles in which I move that in recent years we are seeing more and more salmon carrying scars of earlier wounds, or newer injuries in various stages of healing. The explanation that predators are more plentiful than in former times is rather too simple but no reasonable alternative seems to present itself . . . In the wild, remote river systems of the Atlantic seaboard in Scotland and in North Western Ireland where seals, otters, killer whales, porpoises and all manner of predators are present in inshore waters in relatively large numbers, I thought I saw the results in a high proportion of scarred salmon . . . I would like to know what proportion of scarred fish come to hand in Greenland nets.

9

Whence They Came

Understanding the way a species evolved by tracing its relationships with other species demonstrates how and why it came to occupy the niche it has. It is a useful indication of that species' potential to cope with environmental change and therefore discloses how the species should be managed to best advantage to produce an optimal harvest of catchable fish and, in other circumstances, how it should be conserved.

The evolution of trout and their occupation of western Europe are two separate though inter-related topics which could be sub-titled respectively, ancient and recent history.

An ancient history of the trout is illustrated in Fig 45. To begin we can consider trout and salmon of the genus *Salmo* as a single entity. They and other salmonid cousins shared with the Clupeiformes (herring-like species) a common ancestor in the Ganoid fishes. The ganoids are now extinct, having flourished in the Cretaceous period, between 135 and 65 million years ago. The earliest fish to derive from them on the salmonid line, all of whose members have an adipose fin, were the Salmonoidei which diversified into the Osmeridae (smelts), the Salangidae and the Argentinidae (sail smelts). In another direction the herrings developed from the same rootstock. It is unfortunate that nomenclature is an indispensible part of this history but it is not necessary to retain all the technicalities in one's mind to appreciate it.

The family Salmonidae, our chief concern, was another to evolve from the Salmonoidei at a later stage. It comprises the genus *Coregonus* (whitefish) and *Stenodus*, appropriately called the inconnu, which has a very restricted distribution. The grayling *Thymallus* with its characteristically large dorsal fin is also a member of the Salmonidae. The group of genera known as the Salmonini and encompassing the salmons, trouts and chars also belongs here.

Members of the sub-family Salmonini have a superficially similar shape and external appearance. Their natural range extends around the northern hemisphere, inferring their design to be a successful one. Scientists and naturalists who pondered this diversification of obviously closely-related species and genera from a common rootstock postulated that the Salmonini must originally have been a marine group in order to have achieved such a widespread distribution. It did not seem likely

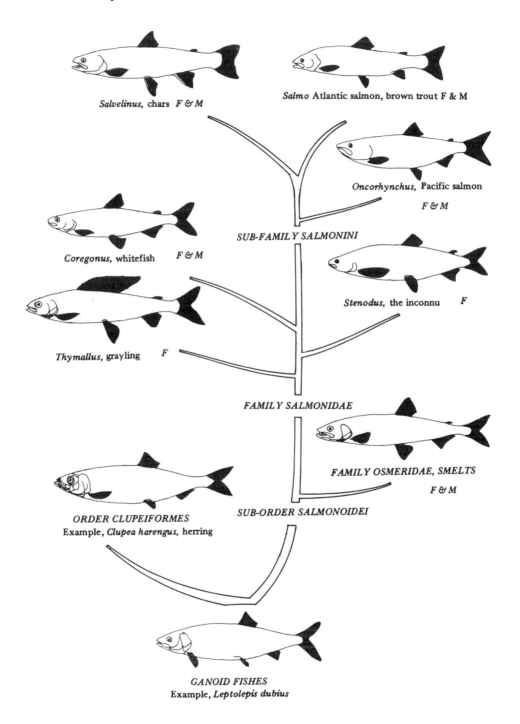

Salvelinus, chars F & M

Salmo Atlantic salmon, brown trout F & M

Oncorhynchus, Pacific salmon

F & M

Coregonus, whitefish   F & M

SUB-FAMILY SALMONINI

Stenodus, the inconnu   F

Thymallus, grayling   F

FAMILY SALMONIDAE

FAMILY OSMERIDAE, SMELTS

F & M

ORDER CLUPEIFORMES
Example, *Clupea harengus*, herring

SUB-ORDER SALMONOIDEI

GANOID FISHES
Example, *Leptolepis dubius*

Fig. 45 Evolutionary relationships among salmonid fishes; F = freshwater and M = marine forms.

that their eggs could have been distributed across expanses of land.

Whether the Salmonini were marine or freshwater in the first instance has been hotly contended. Leaving aside the natural range of the group for a moment, another approach to solving the question might be by considering the habits of its members. In Fig. 45 these are identified as freshwater or marine. Freshwater forms predominate and a minority of them are *also* marine. There are however no exclusively marine genera. This has been regarded as a significant indication of ancestral origin. The fact that some freshwater genera and species have forms which can survive and do very well at sea suggests that salt water was secondarily invaded. None of the Salmonini has to go to sea to complete the life cycle but none can do so in entirely marine conditions. The juvenile stages require freshwater and the eggs must be laid in gravels, suitable examples of which do not occur in the sea.

In the functional sense migratory salmonids descend to the sea in order to make sufficient growth to spawn. The similar purpose of a descent by lake trout to richer feeding conditions is often overlooked. In many aspects of their biology lake and sea trout are identical.

Zoologists in the nineteenth century relied exclusively on anatomical evidence to elucidate relationships among species. Consideration of other sources of information is a relatively new development. In terms of bone structure trout of the genus *Salmo* are more primitive than salmon, and Pacific salmon *Oncorhynchus* are more advanced than either of them. Adaptation to marine conditions is also better exemplified by *Oncorhynchus* whose smolts migrate at a smaller size than do those of the other genus. *Salmo salar* leaves the river at a larger smolt size and returns only to spawn but the smolts of *S. trutta* are larger still and trout may re-enter freshwater several times before maturing. In parallel with anatomical evolution among these fish there would appear to have been a behavioural transition from the entirely freshwater forms of trout through various adaptations to marine conditions.

A perennial problem for scientists has been the development and significance of the smolt stage whose function is to take the juvenile to sea. Exactly how the smolt developed an ability to anticipate circumstances which the juvenile of an entirely freshwater species could not know, was regarded as strong evidence supporting a marine beginning. That is until one realises that the smolt is not essential and that juvenile trout in brown livery can be successfully introduced to salt water. Each autumn these juveniles descend to the sea. Thus, smoltification can be seen as a secondary development in trout rather than a vestige of a marine ancestry.

For the sake of completeness and at the risk of complicating these issues still further, mention should be made of the 'relatively ancestral' role of sea trout in the species *S. trutta*. The dissemination of salmonids through the overland movement of their eggs or young stages by a natural rather than an artificial agency would not have been possible. Instead the various populations, races and strains of the species must have been distributed by a parent invading freshwater systems from the sea. In a previous chapter we saw that resident river trout spawning along with sea trout mature at a smaller size than the sea-run form. The phenomenon of precocity in a species (i.e. sexual maturity in a juvenile) is known as *neoteny*: it is exemplified by the tadpoles of certain Amphibians becoming mature before they metamorphose or change into the adult form. In this sense then, sea trout are more 'adult' than the brownies with which they spawn. This point is worth making. It implies that each strain of sea trout should have a freshwater equivalent — if one knew what to look for or how to identify it.

The degree of diversification which a group of animals has undergone is proportional to the length of its evolutionary history. The Clupeiformes developed from the Ganoid fishes long before the Salmonidae became distinguishable from Clupeids (herrings). It is therefore to the more recent evolutionary history of the trouts that we must refer for an account of the development of races and strains. And we must bear in mind all the time that each trout population occupying a small tributary stream has a unique genetic constitution.

The last great ecological and climatic event in the earth's history was the ice age of the Quaternary (or Recent) period. Its duration was approximately 900,000 years and its cooling effects were global. But it may not have expressed itself in the same way everywhere. Working from deep sea cores, scientists now believe the ice age consisted of nine major stadials or advances of the ice some of which have been recognised in Britain and Ireland. Each of these intervals consisted of periodic extensions of the ice sheets from the north as the air temperature cooled. Later the ice retreated in a period of atmospheric warming. Less extreme stadials and sub-stadials had the effect of freezing the valleys of the higher mountains only.

At the maximum influence of the ice age the greater part of Britain and Ireland was covered by a massive ice sheet. Because so much water was locked up in the glaciers, sea level was lower and the coastline was farther out to sea than at present. Underneath the ice sheets the islands of Ireland and Britain were united across what is now the north Irish Sea. The main freshwater drainage for Ireland and Britain at this time was southwards by the gigantic Celtic River basin. The rivers which at present flow south and eastwards in the south-east of Ireland and those which drain to the west and southwards in Britain were its tributaries (Fig. 46).

While the northern and western areas of Ireland and Britain were effectively sterilised under an enormous ice sheet, we can assume that many of its frozen rivers were devoid of fish life which gradually reestablished once the ice retreated. The ice withdrew not in a single sweep

'Celtic River' basin

*Fig. 46 Britain and Ireland at the maximum extent of the ice sheets.
The distribution of the Celtic salmon race is shown in black.*

but in a series of retractions. Each of these in Britain and Ireland was contemporaneous with equally momentous events in other parts of western Europe. As the western and northern parts of Britain and Ireland became free of ice and therefore receptive to immigrations of fish from the sea, the ice-bound parts of Europe, where races of trout had been isolated to develop distinctive characteristics and attributes for perhaps twenty thousand years, thawed. Once the ice blockade was lifted these races and strains were liberated to sally forth and colonise other river and lake systems from the sea.

The current distribution of fish life in Britain and Ireland is explicable in these terms. Only species which could make the migration through salt water on their own came as far as Ireland, the first major island to break with the European continent when the ice melted and sea water levels rose. These were entirely salmonids; cyprinids (coarse fish) which have little tolerance of marine conditions, were imported by man much later.

Then, as the climate continued to ameliorate some salmonids which had flirted with the edge of the retreating ice sheets were left in the isolated lakes and rivers of their newly settled territories. Rising temperatures may be the explanation for their loss of *anadromy* (the habit of running to sea to feed and back to freshwater to spawn) which characterises many of the salmonids at present established in the lower latitudes. Today *Salvelinus* (char) is represented by a number of almost sealed-off populations in mountain lakes; further north they run to sea. The same is true of *Coregonus* (whitefish), and recent biochemical analysis has established that *Coregonus pollan* in Britain and Ireland is the same species as *Coregonus autumnalis* of Alaska which regularly runs to sea to feed. The Mediterranean basin is fringed by resident brown trout populations which must have been established there during cooler times but whose members do not go seawards any more.

For brown trout the last one hundred thousand years have been a period of great diversification. As the ice sheets melted and proffered more freshwater for colonisation, hitherto closed freshwaters were opened up and their inmates released to the outside world. Forms such as the gillaroo, to which reference has already been made, first identified by naturalists and anglers in the nineteenth century and subsequently authenticated by modern biochemical methods of recognising fish strains, was one of these.

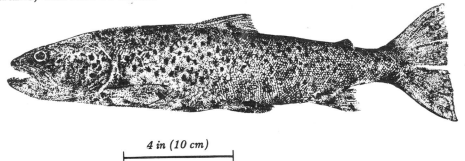

4 in (10 cm)

Fig. 47 A ferox *or great lake trout from Lough Melvin. This fish is poorly Conditioned.*

Another was *ferox* trout, beloved of anglers and known with affection and respect by a number of local names such as the Great lake trout, the Buddah and the Big fat fellow. For a time, earlier in this century, *ferox* were regarded with some scepticism as an artefact of the nineteenth century imagination but these trout have been re-accorded respectability in the wake of a more critical appraisal of their biology, behaviour and their chemical constitution.

Great lake trout or *ferox* were thought to be recognisable by their physical appearance; a long head and prominent teeth (Fig. 47). Like all aspects of trout appearance these are unreliable and *ferox* were not so conveniently pigeon-holed. In retrospect it would appear that some fish attributed to this strain were incorrectly identified. Their other credentials about which there was unanimity included a fish eating habit and large size. And *ferox* never went to sea.

From some of their traditional haunts *ferox* are now departed. Pollution in lakes, for example Lough Neagh, has destroyed their fodder fish and they in turn have succumbed. Recent research has confirmed that their remaining haunts are large lakes (those larger than 1,000 acres (400 hectares)) where a suitable prey fish species is present in quantity, and recent investigations have associated a particular biochemical compound with the fish.

This biochemical compound known as the LDH 5 allele has been identified using electrophoresis but its functional significance is unknown. It occurs at a high incidence in trout which have a long life expectancy, *ferox* and long-lived sea trout being two of these.

The possibility of a close relationship between long-lived sea trout and *ferox* is worth examining more closely and for this reason the occurrence of the two has been plotted in Fig. 48. Their distribution pattern suggests that the *ferox* form is a resident (purely freshwater) trout which came to these islands by sea through the agency of the long-lived sea trout. In other words that these two forms are variants of the same race.

The LDH 5 allele is an ancient genetic constituent of salmonids which has been identified in rainbow trout and salmon as well as brown trout. For this reason trout which have it are assumed to be closer to the salmonid rootstock than those which have 'lost' the chemical. Thus both *ferox* and long-lived sea trout, which, because they both possess it, could be regarded as genetically closely related, are relatively more ancient than the other sea trout strain(s) which no longer possess it.

And there are other, at first sight, unlikely strains of trout which do. These are the stunted trout living in mountainous regions, in very much the same kind of topography as the *ferox* and long-lived sea-run trout. This instantly prompts the question why these trout with such potential for growth should be stunted. To which the answer: large size in trout depends on two things, one the genetic constitution (possession of the LDH 5 allele) and second the existence of sufficient food to fuel growth. The stunted trout have the first of the two but, in their small mountain streams they lack adequate food to express their long lives in large size.

If the possessors of the LDH 5 allele are an ancient form of trout it is very likely that they were among the first of the trout strains to occupy Britain and Ireland when the ice sheets began their retreat, and yet today the distribution of these fish is very discontinuous although it is in a pattern along the western seaboard of Britain and Ireland. Similar forms are also, or at one time were, widespread in Europe.

To explain how this happened let us digress for a moment to con-

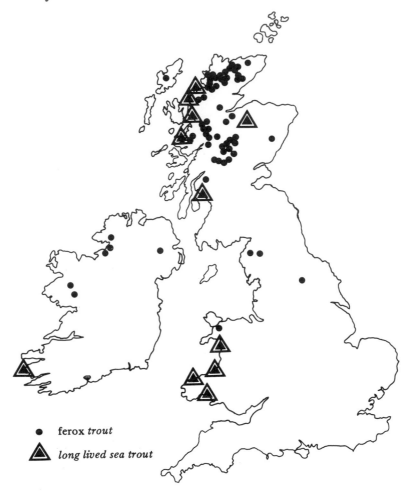

Fig. 48 Records of the occurrence of long-lived sea trout
stocks and of ferox lake trout.

sider stocks of Atlantic salmon. Investigators using electrophoresis have confirmed the existence of at least two races of salmon in Britain and Ireland. One of these, called the *Boreal*, is thought to have originated in northern Europe in much the same way as *ferox* and long-lived sea trout (the two of which we might refer to as Boreal trout), and to have spread southwards when conditions permitted them to occupy the rivers and lakes around the coasts of Britain and Ireland. An exceptional area was that occupied by the tributary streams and rivers draining into the Celtic River basin. In that region a distinctive Celtic strain of salmon may have survived the height of the glaciation; it is still found there today (Fig. 46).

If sea trout have a Boreal equivalent then it might be appropriate to label their short-lived race as *Celtic* stock. And if these short-lived, smaller trout occupied a similar range to the Celtic salmon they might subsequently have been able to extend it once climatic conditions ameliorated. In post-glacial times salmon strains did not encroach very far into one another's territory. It seems very probable that the sea trout did. The Celtic stocks moved northwards and successfully competed with the Boreal race to the detriment of the long-lived fish. Exactly why such a destructive contention occurred is unknown although it has been observed that stocks of the Boreal and Celtic kinds have quite different mating strategies and it has been speculated that in competition the Celtic one would be likely to prove successful.

The terrain in which the Boreal trout triumphed and which they later held as their own, adjoins the mountain fastness of the western coasts of Britain and Ireland. An analysis of catchments containing long-lived sea trout reveals they have cliffs above which stunted trout populations occur. These cliffs (or, less spectacularly, impassable falls), are a further corroboration of the antiquity of these trout stocks which had to penetrate inland before the cliffs formed. Their formation followed the melting of the ice and the elastic spring-back of the land relieved of its ice burden. The impassable falls were an effective drawbridge against any later incoming Celtic trout.

From the upstream stunted trout populations, disdained by anglers and commercial fishermen alike, there is a constant but small leakage of genetic material in the form of small downstream-migrating, probably male trout, which interbreed with incomers from the sea. The progeny of these matings contain the genetic possibilities to reach old age and they are within reach of the medium in which to achieve large size.

And so, to return to the point at which this chapter began, a knowledge of the evolutionary background of these really valuable trout is an indispensable part of knowing how to protect them against manmade forces, however unlikely these might seem. The large lake trout of mainland Europe have been greviously harmed by several artificial influences including the introduction of trout of different strains. Would one ever have thought that the large sea-going trout were ultimately dependent for their survival on insignificant and neglected brown trout living in tiny unfishable becks in the hills?

Three of a Kind

Between freshwater and the ocean European brown trout *Salmo trutta* have in theory a free, even unlimited, range. But nature has imposed constraints; the trout's evolutionary position has governed the size at which it descends to the sea and its sea-run dimensions determine the length of its migration into freshwater. Within these limitations sea trout are adaptable, exploring and exploiting their environment to the maximum. Even the ambivalence of the fish in their frequent movements from one medium to another in their younger marine stages could be regarded as a ploy to utilise both to best advantage. It is instructive to enquire whether *S. trutta* is alone in this life style or whether equivalents — or analogues — of it occur elsewhere.

Within the Salmonini there exists a wide range of life styles from purely freshwater through various degrees of marine. The obvious place to begin looking for an equivalent of sea-run brown trout is among the 'trouts' and two further species propose themselves immediately.

The late nineteenth and early twentieth centuries saw the artificial spread and propagation of *S. trutta* beyond its natural range. Two other species have been similarly transferred to create sport fisheries. The two species are of North American origin from the east and west coasts respectively. Nowadays all three are firmly established in the Americas, Africa, Asia and the Antipodes. Brook trout *Salvelinus fontinalis* and rainbow trout *Salmo gairdneri* both have sea-running forms. The Atlantic Ocean prevented brook trout and brownies from intermixing and a continent intervened between brookies and rainbows, but all three species occupy a similar latitudinal range (Fig. 49). Furthermore, the general biology of all three is very similar so that a knowledge of one should indicate what to expect of the others.

Brook trout *Salvelinus fontinalis*

On the basis of their migratory behaviour there appears to be little reason to consider sea trout hereditarily distinct from freshwater trout. Where trout grow slowly . . . and mature at a small size, they fail to migrate extensively. Where growth is faster the young trout descend from the spawning and rearing areas until they reach suitable conditions. The fact that the first suitable body of water some

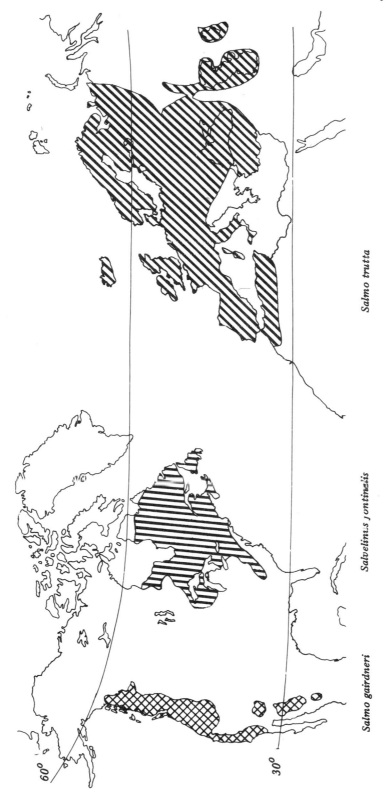

Fig. 49 The natural range of three trout species: Salmo trutta, S. gairdneri *and* Salvelinus fontinalis.

trout reach in their migratory movements is the sea rather than a sufficiently deep cool lake does not indicate hereditary differences in the trout.

These statements written by D.G. Wilder in 1952 summarise essential facts of resident and sea trout biology and emphasise the often over-looked characteristic that the two forms have in common; a journey of some, however brief, length must be made between spawning stream and feeding ground. The whereabouts of their early life and particularly the proximity of the nursery stream to feeding area or sea has at least as much to do with their subsequent life as a genetic influence.

Wilder gave some specific data on sea trout. Their migrations con-sisted of a descent to the estuary in April, May and June and another in the autumn. A first return to freshwater might take place two months after descent in spring and there was a major influx of trout to the rivers in July. On re-entering fresh water the fish virtually ceased feeding. Females predominated among sea-run trout. Many of these facts are characteristic of sea trout but Wilder was not considering the European *Salmo trutta*, but another anadromous species, *Salvelinus fontinalis*, the American brook trout (Fig. 50) whose life history is very similar to that of sea-run *Salmo trutta*. Here are two forms which exploit an identical eco-logical niche, a phenomenon which is not unusual in the animal world. After all, nature abhors a vacuum and niches exist to be filled. What is remarkable is the almost identical life history and behavioural patterns both have adopted to maintain their populations.

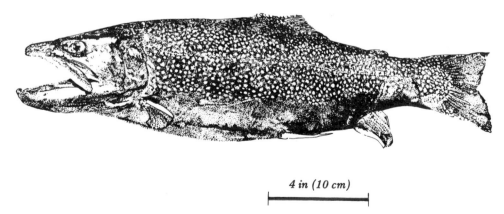

4 in (10 cm)

Fig. 50   A naturalised British brook trout Salvelinus fontinalis.

The genus *Salvelinus,* of which the brook trout is a member, is well represented by a number of distinctive species and sub-species in America and Europe. British chars also belong to the genus which diversified into a number of species during the course of the ice age. Various forms of *S.*

alpinus (char), scattered across western Europe in deep lakes, are believed to have been isolated as the glaciers advanced south and then retreated. *S. fontinalis* was pushed south at the limits of the ice sheets and retained a desire for cooler conditions afterwards. Until man altered its habitat by clearing forests and raising water temperatures the brook trout extended along the east coast of the United States and Canada from Georgia in the south to the Hudson Straits, between latitudes 43° and 65° north.

Brown trout did not occur naturally in North America and their introduction there is quite recent. However its north-south range in Europe is not dissimilar from that of *fontinalis* in North America. Sea-run browns are now confined to the northern part of their distribution although in an earlier, colder age they would have occurred in the Mediterranean Sea.

As on *Salmo trutta*, debate on the relationship of resident and sea-running forms of *Salvelinus fontinalis* raged throughout the nineteenth and early twentieth centuries. Recent thinking has tended towards the belief that both resident and sea-running forms are contained in a single species. Consideration of the details of the life histories of sea run *fontinalis* and *trutta* reveals considerable similarity between them.

Resident and sea-run *fontinalis* and *trutta* have similar spawning habits. As the young trout grow they move downstream until by their second or third year they are likely to occupy still waters. Two year old *fontinalis* smolts attain a fork length of 6.5 in (17 cm) approximately and three year olds 8 in (20 cm). Such dimensions are common to *trutta* smolts also. Spring migrating juveniles of both species smoltify but if the silvered fish are held in freshwater the process is reversed. Brown, un-smolted fish of both species can survive in salt water, silvering up there by deposition of guanin. A sea-run *fontinalis* of fork length 8.9 in (22.6 cm) weighs between 0.26 and 0.28 lb (117 and 127 g) and a British or Irish sea-run *trutta* from the Atlantic coast might well weigh the same so that the two species have a substantially similar shape.

European sea trout are adaptable feeders taking a variety of organisms in the sea but consuming a larger quantity of fish as they grow, a behavioural development to be seen in many salmonid species. In some of their marine feeding areas their choice of food is limited and there *trutta* must make do with a diet of small crustaceans, like amphipods. This feeding pattern is also recorded for *fontinalis*.

Like European sea trout, *fontinalis* is non-discriminating in the freshwater to which it makes a first return. Although *trutta* become more specific about where they choose to spawn their enthusiasm for any freshwater at other times has, more than once, prompted the proposal that they be managed regionally rather than on a single catchment basis.

The reduction of the range of *fontinalis* is a by-product of man's history in North America. At the maximum extent of its natural range its preference for cool waters confined the trout to brooks and springs shaded by giant pine and hemlock trees. Ernest Schwiebert in his monumental work *Trout* tells the story movingly. The large pines with their obvious value in construction were the first and most desirable of the lumber to be cleared when settlers moved into an afforested area. The acid bark of the hemlock was used to cure leather which the Texas trail cattle and the slaughter of the bison herds produced in abundance. Afterwards the waters flowed warmer and the brook trout is currently more successful in parts of the United States outside its natural range, in South America and in the Antipodes.

For several salmonid species water temperature has a critical effect on downstream migration which will not commence until rivers have warmed to a certain threshold. This effect has been recorded in *fontinalis*. Recent work on this species suggests that high estuarine temperatures prove intolerable and drive the fish back into freshwater. Were this common to sea-run brown trout it might have a useful consequence for the fishery manager in, for instance, increasing the proportion of post-smolts to return to freshwater in the year of their first migration, thus boosting the finnock run. Just how narrow is the temperature tolerance of brown trout in the sea is not known but it may be significant that the sea-run form of the fish does not occur on the Mediterranean coast.

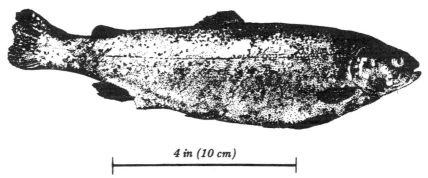

4 in (10 cm)

Fig. 51   A pond reared rainbow trout, Salmo gairdneri.

Rainbow trout *Salmo gairdneri*

Contrasting the swift, agile and muscular Spanish fighting bull with the altogether more ponderous domestic form Ernest Hemingway offered the analogy: 'The fighting bull is to the domestic bull as the wolf is to the dog.' Had he sought the comparison among fish he would have chosen rainbow trout to make the point. Examples of this variable species most frequently encountered are the pond-reared form with its frayed fins and generally drab appearance (Fig. 51) when it is reared in commercial trout farms. *S. gairdneri*, like the European brown trout, is a highly plastic species which, in the past, and to a lesser extent at present, occurs in several distinctive forms which are well adapted to exploit particular environments. Because of their commercial value much more research has been carried out on rainbows than brook trout and a more detailed account of them can be provided.

In the nineteenth century, as was the case for *S. trutta*, rainbow trouts were considered to be a number of distinctive species of which the two major groupings were the resident and sea-going strains. *S. gairdneri*, the steelhead or sea-going form, was considered to have four sub-species. It extended from California as far as British Columbia. As was the case for the European brown trout, there was some validity for this splitting of a species which occurred in a variety of reproductively isolated populations, each distinctive in some small way from the others. But modern taxonomy and terminology slowly extended their influence and a confused list of vaguely defined sub-species was rationalised to two species and then to one.

The transportation of rainbow trout to various parts of the world for sporting and fish farming purposes had meanwhile fostered the proliferation of hatcheries which mixed broodstocks, so that whatever locally distinctive traits there had been were gradually obscured. The nearest to a truly 'resident' strain of rainbow trout, from the Kerin and McCloud Rivers, was absorbed and lost in the subsequent genetic mixture.

The species which is recognised today, *S. gairdneri*, occurs in two forms: steelhead and resident trout. Steelheads are analogous to sea trout and go down to salt water after a juvenile freshwater existence. But some confusion remains. The resident form of the species is said to bolt to sea whenever an opportunity arises and some authorities distinguish between 'sea-run rainbows' and steelheads. Extant strains of rainbows are sea-going from freshwaters close to the coast unless impounded but in many parts of the world the species leads an entirely freshwater existence in lake systems. In many respects it might be said of brown trout, as has been said of rainbows:

> ... (they) migrate to sea at various ages and over a long period within a season, spend varying amounts of time at sea and return over a fairly long period within a season, are capable of spawning more than once and they sometimes spawn before their first migration to sea and may remain in freshwater their entire lives.

As for brown trout and brookies the occurrence of sea-going and resident rainbows conforms to the 'zone' theory which is considered generally applicable to salmonids. Between $57°$ and $34°$ north the species runs to sea; 'resident' or wholly freshwater forms occur at lower latitudes.

Rainbows have been studied in the same way as brown trout and the generally used salmonid terminology describes them. The most detailed analysis of a population is that carried out on Californian steel-heads in 1954. Cross-checking scale readings against scales from fish of known age it was reckoned that 86 per cent of interpretations were correct; this accords well with nine out of ten reported for European sea trout. The term 'smolt' is used to refer to the transitional stage which brings the juvenile down to sea water but, in the case of lake-dwelling rainbows which do not silver up before their descent from the nursery streams, the term is also applied. At the time of leaving flowing for standing waters these juvenile rainbows are said to undergo a physical change and adopt a more migratory appearance which may indeed be analogous to smoltification. Rainbows in the McConaughy Reservoir, Nebraska, were considered 'adult' at a length of 12 in (30 cm); British sea trout would be so described at approximately 12.5 in (32 cm). In short, much of the terminology describing sea-run brown trout is applicable to rainbows.

The stream life of rainbows has much in common with other salmonids which pass their early years in running waters. The eggs are deposited in gravel areas associated with riffles and the young fish move downstream as they grow. Most vigorous growth takes place in the spring and early summer and ceases when the water temperature nears a maximum in midsummer. The sex ratio is one male to one female in two year old fish. Migration to sea or to the richer feeding conditions of lakes takes place at a certain size so the fastest growing individuals leave the streams first. As in brown trout there is a spring and a fall exodus.

The length of the 'smolt' has been given as ranging between 6.9 and 9.8 in (17.5 and 25 cm) in McConaughy Reservoir, Nebraska, and similar limits have been reported for steelheads in California. Many sea trout stocks smoltify within these extremes. The age at which these dimensions are reached by rainbows is about two years. In a study in Lake Huron 99 per cent of smolts were two year olds; however as many as 92 per cent of one year olds have been reported in a smolt class. It is generally recognised that the usual response to higher latitude is an extension of parr life so that, as in brown trout as one goes northwards, the parr life lengthens.

In at least one important respect *S. gairdneri* differs from *S. trutta*: at a given fork length it weighs heavier. In shape rainbows are deeper and they will always outweigh sea trout of the slim-bodied, Atlantic feeding type of the same length; some of the well Conditioned sea trout from the Irish Sea would run them fairly close.

Most steelheads from the Puget Sound in the State of Washington mature after two years and approximately one-third after three years in the sea. This rate of maturation in fish which migrated mainly as two year smolts is very similar to the situation prevailing in British and Irish sea trout stocks. In making sea growth the fish migrate mostly short distances — one study gives 19 miles (30 km) as the maximum recorded journey — and, in accordance with what is emerging for *S. trutta* (though contrary to what was widely believed at one time), 98 per cent of steelheads return to their river of origin. A larger size at first migration improves their chance of surviving to return.

In Europe brown trout (and this includes the sea-run form) spawn between early October and late November but this pattern is not immutable. In the sub-Antarctic Kerguelen Islands to which brown trout have been introduced, reproduction takes place over nine months of the year. A long spawning period by rainbows therefore is a difference of degree rather than kind between the species. Rainbow trout, additionally, are credited with having distinctive spawning races which co-exist in the same system without interbreeding. They differ in their time of entry to the river and their period of egg-laying. In the Capilano River, British Columbia, winter running fish enter the streams between December and March while the summer runners enter between May and early August. Winter runners are about to spawn at time of arrival in freshwater while the summer fish will not do so until the following March or April. These may be described in the terminology (now defunct) for *S. irideus* which bred in the spring months and *S. shasta* which made up the bulk of the importations of rainbows to England and which spawned in the autumn. The introduced rainbows of Lake Huron entered their spawning rivers, either between October and February when they spawned between December and February, or from February to April in which case spawning took place at once. The fish which composed these two runs were quite different in their age class composition and size.

The migrations of steelheads in California comprise a spring run which is composed of large fish up to 12 lb (5.5 kg) in weight, similar in that respect to spring run *S. trutta*. They enter the streams on falling water levels, rest up in pools in June and July and spawn the following November and December. Fall fish enter the streams on rising water levels in July and August and they return to sea within four months of spawning.

By the time rainbows reach maturity the sex ratio has begun to alter and males have declined in the population. Among the younger spawning age groups males are more numerous but females predominate among the older rainbows. In McConaughy Reservoir, Nebraska, females were twice as numerous as males in the total population. However, supplementary males (precocious parr) probably redress the ratio at spawning time. Males enter the spawning tributaries before females and the female digs six or seven redds in the course of spawning.

Steelhead trout are not thought to resume feeding after spawning until they have regained salt water and this is also probably true of *S. trutta*. Although there are exceptions both species do not necessarily forsake freshwater at once and may rest for a time before making their way downstream.

The predilection of rainbows for marine conditions has led some scientists to find an explanation in the foods that are available there. Like all trout and salmon fry juvenile rainbows concentrate on zooplankton and minute aquatic organisms. Their growth is rapid and they soon turn to the diet common to larger salmonids, a diet which includes small shoalfish. For the smaller crustaceans and aquatic insects, rainbows never lose their liking completely and in this respect they are unusual.

Some workers quote the fact that planktonic forms are abundant in the sea as the reason for the rainbow's migration and there is a marked difference in feeding response between *gairdneri* and *trutta* where the two co-exist in the wild. In a sea lough on the North Irish coast rainbows which had escaped from sea cages displayed a marked preference for small particulate foods: crustaceans, insects and fragments of vegetation. Sea-run brown trout also consumed these foods but concentrated on organisms of larger size, notably containing in their stomachs more fish remains than did rainbows. Their preference for small particulate food is indisputably true of rainbow trout although as the reason for their going to sea it is hardly convincing; the same could after all be said of brown trout which feed on larger prey. The truth is most likely that both species descend to the richer feeding in salt water in order to make growth for reproduction.

Thus, we see in two further inshore dwelling species of salmonids, one of them not even belonging to the same genus as brown trout, identical strategems of coping with a freshwater and marine existence. In evolutionary terms the phenomenon would be described as *convergence*, which signifies the approach to a similar form and life style of species which had different evolutionary origins. Convergence was so convincing for *Salvelinus fontinalis* that although this trout belongs to a different genus and is therefore only distantly related to *Salmo trutta*, the two were at one time thought to be the same species.

European sea trout then are well adapted to the kind of life style they follow. When other fish have attempted to fill the same ecological niche they have done so in identical fashion although they are not related to brown trout and have evolved at a great distance from them. The message is that such details of the life cycles of these species which remain to be satisfactorily explained are certain to have a functional significance. Nature could not afford to experiment with futile design and gamble with prodigal life style.

11

The Last Link in the Food Chain

As the less important of the two British sea-going species of *Salmo*, the exploitation of sea trout by man is not nearly so precisely documented as salmon. Occasional references to trout do occur in a scattered literature but so few are they that a comprehensive and detailed account is not feasible.

Our approach to the subject will be conducted along the following lines. First, the main events in game conservation in Britain and Ireland up to the eighteenth century will be recounted. The review will attempt to identify principles governing animal conservation generally. Salmon fisheries will be accorded special attention from the eighteenth century in Ireland and, because so few specific references to sea trout are made, the management of salmonid fisheries in a predominantly sea trout-producing region, Connemara, will be examined in detail.

The exploitation of any living species is a consequence of several factors: its biology, the technology available and the social attitudes prevailing at a particular time. The last is the most critical of the three and, for reasons which will become apparent, it is difficult to decipher in the Irish context. What documentation is available would suggest that game preservation was a more serious preoccupation in Britain and, as England has had a hand in Irish affairs since the twelfth century, a brief consideration of the British experience would be a useful starting point.

Although the Romans are believed to have practised a rudimentary conservation policy in Britain — insofar as they introduced pheasant and fallow deer and presumably provided some kind of protection until these species became established — game preservation did not come into prominence until the tenth and eleventh centuries. In medieval times game had an economic justification, supplementing the diet in the winter months when domestic animal production was low. In the course of setting aside deer forests William the Conqueror cleared villages and vested the hunting rights in himself. By the thirteenth century the forest laws had become a major contention which the barons sought to have resolved by Magna Carta. The power of the monarchy was weakened then but hunting remained a prerogative of the nobility. Hunting was after all the image of war, a suitable occupation for those who, according to the rules of chivalry, had little better to do with their time. And conservation policies were more successful in England than in France because the monarchy was stronger in England during Norman times. It is an important principle in conservation practice that the strongest party considers the resource primarily his and it has been expressed in various modified forms since. In the eighteenth century Christian, the judge and Cambridge professor, could, in keeping with the extension of the principle that nobility hunted and the poacher was by definition a lower form of creation, describe the latter as: 'He who sleeps by day and prowls for food in the night, soon acquiring the disposition of a savage or a wild beast.'

In spite of the efforts of the Normans and their successors, progressive disafforestation (of deer forests) continued until Charles I tried to revive the forest laws and ceremonies as a means of increasing his wealth in 1634. It was a move which occasioned a deep resentment, recollected when the Civil War broke out and poaching became widespread. When in 1651 the deer forests were vested in trustees and in 1653 a proposal to 'manage the forests of the King less offensively to the people' was presented to the Council of State the preoccupation with deer was largely over. The ensuing war with the Dutch was accompanied by slaughter of game and stripping of forests so that it was necessary to restock the deer parks with animals imported from the Continent.

As deer ceased to be such a contentious issue the emphasis passed to small game and in 1671 the Cavalier Parliament introduced a property qualification to shoot. In the latter half of the eighteenth century fifty-three acts of parliament were directed against the ordinary poaching of small game, whose disappearance was hastened by the development of the light flintlock and the intensification of agriculture. In time this corpus of legislation came to be regarded as more severe than the medieval forest laws. Paradoxically poaching became widespread — and profitable — and the violence associated with it made it unsafe for a sportsman to venture out alone. In response, the *battue* or mass shoot was devised, poachers formed co-operatives to pay fines for one another and alternative forms of hunting, as for foxes, became fashionable. For some land owners in the eighteenth century (the Earls of Uxbridge are a good illustration) game preservation was an all-consuming preoccupation monopolising their correspondence and in 1831 one-sixth of all legal convictions in England and Wales were for poaching offences.

In 1827 the game laws were relaxed and four years later the Game Act abolished the archaic land qualification and also permitted anyone with a firearms certificate to shoot. It also abolished the harsher penalties associated with poaching. In spite of these reforms the question of game preservation remained a highly contentious one occasioning considerable social friction for the remainder of the century.

Documentary evidence shows that angling was an established

gentlemanly pursuit as early as the fourteenth century. By the eighteenth the resource was still in good condition and fishing was easily obtained by the ordinary people. The adequate supply meant that fishing was not associated with the social conflict which characterised the imposition of the game laws. And while the sale of game was prohibited there was no comparable ban on the sale of fish. The Black Act of 1723 which allowed the death penalty for a number of poaching offences was not particularly associated with the taking of fish. In fact this controversial legislation had been introduced to deal with a series of offences, including the raiding of carp ponds, committed by a particular gang, the Waltham Blacks, who practised a variety of crimes at night, with blackened faces.

Undoubtedly, Ireland's salmon fisheries would have benefited from this tranquil climate had it not been for one additional fact whose impact it is difficult to assess. Ireland was a conquered country and agrarian protests such as the maiming of cattle were well known in the late eighteenth century although there is no evidence that destruction of fisheries was a part of these. As recently as 1970 Republican Publications could recommend poaching as a form of protest which '. . . must be actively supported . . .'. It is a view reminiscent of the fourteenth century act of impaling a deer's head on a stake and facing it towards the sun, its mouth open, an insult to the king.

The administrative background

Until the end of the eighteenth century the exploitation of salmonids was probably to some extent carried out by rod and line but commercial fishermen also operated nets and traps by public right and also by grant conferred prior to Magna Carta. Heavy pressure on stocks of salmon is thought to have commenced with the introduction of the *stake net* to the River Spey in Scotland in 1797. Ten years later it made its appearance in Keem Bay, Achill Island in Ireland. It would appear that stake nets were fairly similar to *bag nets*. They were large, fixed labyrinthine traps of netting into which the fish wandered and from which they did not know how to escape. They fished automatically and were constructed of netting which may have been selective for salmon. They were highly effective at capturing this species, rapidly depleting stocks in the systems they fished and in their neighbouring catchments. Although there are adequate data to illustrate the depredations of these engines* on salmon, there are only sporadic references to sea trout catches. One of these (provided by Francis Day) was to the fisheries of the River Tweed whose grilse and salmon catch declined in the first fifty years of the nineteenth century by two-thirds, while the sea trout catch declined by only one-

Engine is a term used to describe a method of capture such as rod and line, bag net, etc. A description of the most important engines is given in Chapter 12.

fifth. The weight of the catch is regarded as indicative of the state of health of the stocks.

The success of stake netting prompted the spread of this engine, a move which the general climate of lawlessness in the wake of the 1798 Rebellion in Ireland fostered. By 1835 the detrimental effects of these nets were so widely appreciated that a Royal Commission was convened to enquire into the state of the industry. The Commission which reported the following year concluded that salmon fisheries were in a poor state and the Act of 1842 was the response to the crisis.

The formulation of the 1842 Act contained some additional features which were special to Irish circumstances. Its provisions were drawn up by prominent Irish politicians, including Daniel O'Connell, who were described as 'thoroughly representative of the conflicting claims of territorial ownership and of the general public'.

The Act as it applied to Ireland differed in one important respect from its operation in Britain: in Ireland it recognised a public right to fish (Section 65):

> ... in places where a public right of fishing for salmon with such nets, in the nature of a common of piscary, has been enjoyed for a space of twenty years next before the passing of this Act.

The provision suggests a degree of social cohesion in Ireland which was not apparent in Britain.

The 1842 Act gave the right to erect nets to owners and occupiers of land adjoining the sea and estuaries, contrary to the evidence collected by the 1835 Commission. So harmful were the effects of the widespread netting which ensued that within six years six different Acts were passed in an effort to repair the damage, culminating in 1848 with an Act which set up boards of conservators and provided for the licensing of all methods of capture. This however had the effect of increasing the number of nets still further although the additional engines which made their appearance were licensed. Finally in 1863 a further Act came into force which restricted certain engines.

The 1863 Act of Parliament had been promoted by the sporting lobby and particularly by the proprietors of the upper riverine reaches. It is from about this time that the first catch records of a sea trout sport fishery (Screebe in Connemara, Fig. 52) date and its total annual yield to the rod in the mid nineteenth century was much the same as today.

If the proprietors' lobby was strong and influential in Britain and Ireland, the number of licensed anglers in Ireland was not large; it did not consistently exceed 3,000 for a period of ten years until 1913 and that level of licence sales was depressed by civil unrest later. Another question, how accurate an indicator of angling intensity such licence figures might be, is a matter of conjecture.

The 1863 Act of Parliament overcame the problem of stake netting

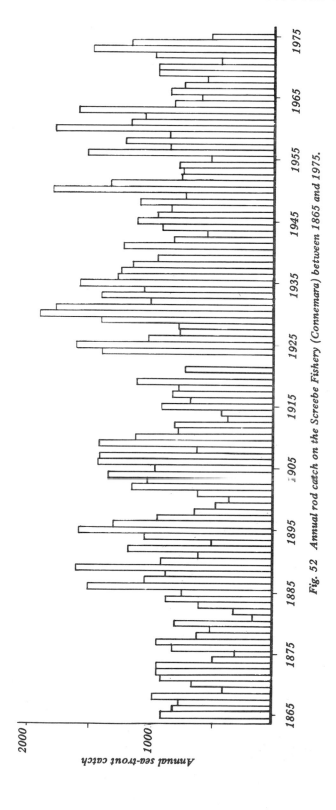

Fig. 52 Annual rod catch on the Screebe Fishery (Connemara) between 1865 and 1975.

in the estuaries but it opened the possibility of draft (seine netting) upstream. A draft net is a length of meshing which is set around one or more fish and then drawn into the shore enclosing the catch. In 1862 there were 463 licensed draft nets and this number increased to 1,020 in thirty years. Drift nets operate by 'gilling' or wedging the fish in the netting, licences issued for them rose from 36 to 394 in the same period and snap nets which are hand operated to capture individual fish increased by 47. Of these three methods the most potentially detrimental to sea trout is draft netting which, because it is an enclosing rather than an enmeshing mechanism (which would probably be size selective for fish of salmon dimensions), will ordinarily retain sea trout of two sea summers' growth and, with a smaller mesh, will hold post-smolts. Again there is a great dearth of information on the actual impact of the increase in the use of draft nets on sea trout. Francis Day has given some data which suggest that in one fishery between 1868 and 1884 the salmon catch declined by three-quarters whereas the sea trout catch increased threefold. If these figures could be taken to indicate the strengths of the respective stocks, sea trout would seem to have done quite well on the arrangement!

The continuing decline of salmon was reviewed by a Select Committee of Enquiry in 1884 and by another in 1899. The latter recorded for the first time a decrease in trout stocks, including those of brown trout. Disturbances associated with the Irish Civil War of 1922 were followed by a further increase in netting and in 1928 the number of licences for commercial engines in the Irish Free State was 1,833; for the whole of Ireland in 1921 it had been 1,088.

The first Fisheries Commission of the Republic held in 1933 expressed similar concerns to those voiced by the Commission of thirty-five years previously. In the words of one commentator:

> All (the members of the Commission) agreed that there was a decline in the numbers of fish and all ascribed the decline to causes other than that associated with their own particular activities.

A second Commission was convened in 1970; once more concern was expressed for the state of stocks although some of the emphasis was directed away from inshore salmon fisheries to the newly developing exploitation on the high seas. The methods in use there however were specifically directed at salmon and the sea trout would appear to have entered the twentieth century at least no worse off than the larger species and probably a great deal healthier. In 1887 Francis Day could describe the methods of capturing sea trout at sea as mackerel drift nets, mullet nets, drifting har g nets (all of these *gilling* nets) at the mouths of rivers and draft (or seine) nets in sandy bays. It is a list which has been repeated by many workers since and precise details of the depredations of these methods still remain to be supplied.

The social context

Effective conservation policy for a living resource must satisfy three criteria: adequate legislation, ownership and public co-operation. Throughout the nineteenth century there was an awareness of the problems confronting salmon fisheries but the zeal of earlier British conservation policy was not displayed, perhaps fortunately as such efforts were frequently counter-productive. The ownership criterion was fulfilled by the landlord system which confined the possession of the land to very few, but the prevailing public attitude, in the absence of the kind of detailed records which survived the Earls of Uxbridge, can only be surmised. However it would seem that for a variety of reasons the control of exploitation of the resource was haphazard and there were other negative forces in operation. In addition to the disorder following the 1798 Rebellion and the agitation accompanying the Land War in the later years of the next century, the very real need for food in the later Famine years must have imposed a considerable stress on spawning and easily accessible salmonids.

We have seen that pressures on salmonid stocks began to increase in the early nineteenth century, a period which saw a rapid increase in population in both Ireland and Britain. In Britain the population increase was sustained by a rise in industrialisation but in Ireland the availability of a single crop, the potato, provided the necessary sustenance. Between 1780 and the outbreak of the potato Famine the population increased dramatically. In 1782 Grattan had told a new parliament 'Ireland is now a Nation' and succeeding years saw a rise in nationalistic feeling. Social conditions were not easy. A report in 1836 estimated the number of labourers unemployed for more than thirty weeks of the year at half a million and their dependants four times as many. Poverty was the main social problem and potential solutions to it included emigration, a poor law, public relief works and land reform. In such circumstances the morale of the people is unlikely to have been high and undoubtedly Thomas Carlyle's account of the Irishman '. . . in his squalor and unreason, in his falsity and drunken violence, as the readymade nucleus for degradation and disorder . . .' had some adherents. Sir Walter Scott on the other hand described the Irishman's 'national condition' as 'turned towards gaiety and happiness' and there is much evidence that this view was widely held. Perhaps the truth lay somewhere in between, a mixture of contradictions '. . . a blend of courage and evasiveness, tenacity and inertia, loyalty and double dealing'.

In 1841 at least four-fifths of the population was rural and living under the landlord system, and 40 per cent subsisted in one-roomed mud cabins. Some landlords were benevolent, others were not, but precise information on the attitudes of tenant to landlord, crucial to an evaluation of public support for fishery conservation, is not available. The

Devon Commission which reported in 1845 concluded that relations between landlord and tenant were a cause of unrest in the country although more recent historians have tended to regard the landlord system as generally considerate of its tenantry. Wherever the truth lies, the century opened in the wake of the abortive 1798 Rebellion and the memory of the earlier French Revolution must have remained an unsettling influence throughout. The rise in nationalism and land hunger culminated in the agitation of the 1880s of which the Captain Boycott incident is an enduring memory.

W.H. Maxwell in his book *Wild sports of the West* described night poaching with gaff and torch as widespread in the west of Ireland in the early nineteenth century:

> Hundreds of breeding fish are annually thus destroyed and although the greater fisheries may be tolerably protected, it is impossible to secure the mountain streams from depredation. If detected the legal penalty for poaching is trifling, and . . . appeals on very frivolous grounds are allowed.

The partial failure of the potato crop in 1845 marked the commencement of the Famine and from then until the introduction of the Poor Law and its assistance schemes in 1847 the British Government behaved with generosity towards the country. However, Britain herself was going through financial difficulties in 1847 and the official attitude towards Ireland, with which at least some landlords were probably identified in the public mind, became more severe. It was in this period that local incidents of intimidation and murder increased.

Because the capital for investment in sea going boats was not available the Famine years saw the paradox of thousands starving on the coast and plentiful shoals of marine fish unharvested. It can be assumed that a population subsisting on 'old cabbage leaves, roadside weeds, rotten turnips, edible seaweed and raw limpets' would have relished illegally captured salmon and trout.

By 1870 when some kind of post-Famine stability had been achieved more than half the country was managed by 800 landlords and even though agricultural production and prices were high and the incidence of agrarian unrest low, the land war erupted. *Scotch loch fishing* by 'Black Palmer' published in 1882, contained the following:

> Some parts of Ireland are famous for their sea trout fishing and though we have never been there ourselves, we mean to go some day when the Land Bill has pacified the natives and made them law abiding subjects. Meantime one runs the risk of being mistaken for a non-resident landlord, and that would be a pity for one's wife and family.

The annual reports of the Inspectors of Irish Fisheries record an increased incidence of poaching offences coinciding with the land agitation. As the 1880s progressed their frequency declined annually. During these later years of the century poaching by poisoning freshwaters with the sap of the plant known as the Irish spurge (*Euphorbia hyberna*) and with lime is frequently alluded to in the reports but there is no similarly detailed account available for comparison from the early years of the century.

The other element in conservation policy, or its absence, was the attitude of the landlords; while this could be expected to favour the resource, an unsettled tenantry (if such was the case) would have discouraged a strict preservation policy. To this must be added the reputation for absenteeism and Regency fecklessness which were associated with some landowners during the earlier years of the century when some of the gentry 'decayed in an atmosphere of laziness, generosity and treachery'.

It is of course possible that the majority (or a sizeable minority) of Irish landlords had as little sympathy for the necessity of protecting the resources under their jurisdiction as the worst of their tenants. Maxwell in his *Wild sports of the West* recounts what may have been a widespread practice:

> The commander, too, talked in good, set terms of 'honourable conduct' but precept and practice, I lament to say, are somewhat irreconcilable. 'Andy' he said, in a most insinuating manner, to our attendant: 'Andy bawn, you were always an obliging boy, and very handy with the gaff. Just keep your eye on the banks as we go along: and if you can snaffle a salmon or two, why, the pannier will tell no tales and weigh all the heavier.'

Maxwell's *Wild sports of the West* was written about Co. Mayo. Lord Dunraven in an introduction to the book described the West generally as a region in which the King's writ did not run and instead custom, the unwritten law of the master sanctioned by illegal physical force prevailed, supporting the view of the 'hard riding, hard drinking, duelling, lavishly hospitable landed gentry, ruling over contented tenants'.

A similar description has been applied to the Martins of neighbouring Co. Galway whose estates included the 200,000 acres of rock, bog and water which contain the Connemara sea trout fisheries. The estate had a steady income from salmon and oysters and Richard Martin who inherited in 1794 was a Commissioner of Fisheries. In other respects the finances of the estate in the nineteenth century were poor. The Martins spoke Irish, maintained close ties with the peasantry and were thought to be in league with smugglers and of being sympathetic to the 1798 Rebellion. During the Famine years the estate went bankrupt and passed into other hands. This coincided with the collapse of the Clifden Union which administered the poor law in Connemara.

If poaching occurred in the Connemara area it was probably prompted by need or greed but without the element of political protest and defiance which might have incited systematic and widespread destruction. Seamus Mac Con Iomaire described the marine life of Connemara in 1938. He wrote in Irish so he would presumably have been able to penetrate the web of contradictions ascribed to the Irish character by various observers. Roughly translated Mac Con Iomaire's account of local attitudes to sea trout reads as follows:

> The British had a law that there should be no netting of any bay where salmon or sea trout were being angled for . . . The British Government tried to exterminate gulls and cormorants in these bays and they paid a bounty of three pence a head on each bird. The fishermen had little time for sea trout and salmon. They would much prefer pollock or cod and they could not understand these British laws which were safeguarding the salmon. When bailiffs apprehended them for fishing they would explain that few salmon or sea trout were caught in their nets. But this was no use because the bailiffs would bring them to court and they would be heavily fined or get a long imprisonment. So the fishermen paid no attention to the bounty for seabirds.

Historical milestones are most confidently identified in retrospect and when Kingsmill Moore published *A man may fish* in 1960 he could look back over thirty years of sea trout angling in Connemara; he described his quarry in the following terms:

> The white trout of Connemara are not large. In this district I have taken only one fish of four pounds and not more than a couple of dozen of three pounds or over. Two pounders are fairly plentiful. Herling run from half a pound to three quarters . . . with a large basket — indeed with any basket of over a dozen — it is almost impossible to exceed an average of two pounds . . .

In spite of this view, which such catch records as exist corroborate, J.P. Digby in 1951 wrote:

> It is common knowledge that in the Connemara area, where agreement to forego netting has been in existence for a long period, the size of the sea trout has seriously deteriorated until a day's bag will contain a large percentage of fish which would have been released by the angler of forty years ago. Not only have sea trout deteriorated in size through the competition of salmon for spawning space but well known lakes . . . (are) no longer worth fishing.

However Digby acknowledged that poaching problems in the area were minimal:

> . . . With the exception of some two or three seasons' commercial netting in the estuary which took place during the first world war

no commercial capture of fish has taken place in the fishery for more than fifty years. Not only are the salmon completely free from the inroads made in other areas but perhaps nowhere in the world and certainly nowhere in this country are spawning fish better protected than in the upper Connemara fishery district, of which the Ballinahinch fishery forms the greater part . . .

Throughout the nineteenth century and possibly into the early years of the twentieth, one of the main preoccupations in protecting salmonids was preventing the removal of the spawning fish from the redds. This poaching tradition had probably started during the Famine and is believed to have decreased in recent times. A method of countering these depredations was to impose a patrol on the most important spawning streams. One-roomed watchers' huts were built on vulnerable parts of the fisheries. In the earlier years of their existence they were thatched, latterly roofed with corrugated iron or slates. Their use now is as luncheon places for anglers. The occurrence of these huts in the Connemara Fishery District is shown in Fig. 53. A few buildings are noted on the six inch to one mile Ordnance Survey maps which were revised in 1898 but the majority must have been constructed some time later.

Memories of better angling times are a kind of reality to be contended with and precise knowledge of what has gone before can be reassuring. We will never know to what extent sea trout stocks suffered long-term damage or indeed what pressure they had to sustain in the nineteenth century. What strands of information have come down to us suggest that sea trout received less attention from fishermen than salmon and that sea trout could more easily bear the kinds of pressure exerted.

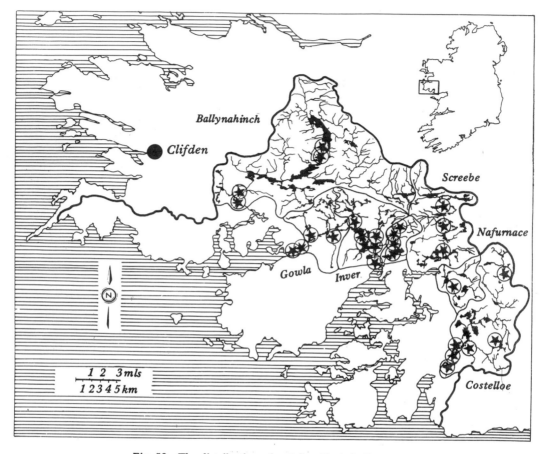

Fig. 53   The distribution of watchers' huts in Connemara.

12

The Ones That Did Not Get Away

Fishing, whether by rod and line or net (either enclosing or meshing), has remained basically unchanged for many hundreds of years, although modern materials have enabled the more effective operation of the engines concerned and, with the intensification of fisheries, statistics relating to capture have been collected with more enthusiasm. But in spite of all the effort which has been put into gathering data since the turn of the century there is still much uncertainty about the size of the catch. Accurate statements about sea trout exploitation are simply not available from much of Britain and Ireland and one can but make fairly sweeping deductions from limited case histories. Once more these points will be made with reference to sea trout fisheries in Ireland. Many of the conclusions are likely to be valid elsewhere.

Concerning the availability of catchable fish: we have already seen that sea trout produce a surplus of eggs to ensure that every feeding opportunity is utilised by their juveniles. The divided migration from and return of the fish to freshwater ensures a fairly constant supply for harvest over the short term. And, in rod fisheries, exploited by a low density of anglers the catch would seem to be a small proportion of the total available. Comparisons of catch and stock have been made in only a few instances but these demonstrate that the varying levels of stock from year to year do not greatly influence the angling yield although the age profile of the population does affect the quality — notably the average weight — of the catch.

One way of judging angling performance is to consider the output of a specific fishery and we have already seen that the rod and line returns from the Screebe fishery suggest a stable yield over a long period.

In Ireland the next source of information to be consulted is the official returns made by licensed fishermen using nets and rods. By law, since 1927 the holders of such licences are required to report their catches. In fact a minority do. Only about 5 per cent of rod fishermen return details of their catch and the interpretation of these has for long been a contentious issue. Recent critical appraisals suggest that only the more successful rod fishermen are prepared to volunteer information about their catches and that the bags of trout taken by these fishermen may amount to a substantial proportion of the total landings. The usual method of arriving at total catch estimates has been to ascertain the weight of catch per angler who reports and multiply this by the total number of licences issued. If the angling fraternity thus tends to have its landings overstated, constraints on the commercial sector might well persuade it to understate its share of the catch.

For all its imperfections the estimation of catches from partial returns has provided data which are fairly consistent on a year to year basis. Total landings of sea trout averaged about 25 tonnes* annually between 1927 and 1950. From 1950 they increased along with the sales of rod licences to a maximum of about 60 tonnes and they have fluctuated over the last ten years between 40 and 60 tonnes per year. Taking two recent years: in 1980 the total landings of sea trout amounted to 59 and the following year to 50 tonnes. To the nearest tonne these were distributed among the following methods of capture:

	1980	*1981*
Rod:	51	40
Draft net:	8	8
Drift net:	less than 1	2

On the basis of estimates such as these, sea trout have been described as a 'sporting' rather than a 'commercial' fish but that assumption could be queried, if not overturned, by a more intimate scrutiny of the sources of information on which the figures are based.

One might suppose that if such fundamentals as the division of the catch among the major methods of capture were in dispute there would be little prospect of pursuing the subject further but, on the contrary, a large lode of data is there to be mined. The enquiries are local rather, than national and while they will not resolve nagging doubts about the total catch they give important indications of the trend in captures by all three methods. These are incidentally the most important means of taking sea trout. Other engines such as snap nets are also effective but their contribution to the total is minimal.

Salmon drift nets

As they are at present fished salmon drift nets would seem to exert a relatively small impact on sea trout. These nets hang from the water surface and drift with the currents. Fish strike a curtain of net and wedge in a single mesh. Often this grips and retains the fish about the gills. For this reason they are also known as *gill nets*. A variety of materials have been used to make drift nets, the older or *multifilament* natural fibres having been replaced by synthetic *monofilament* netting in recent years. Monofilament is very difficult to see in the water and for this

---

*One metric tonne is approximately equivalent to an imperial ton; only the former is given.

reason it fishes very effectively and, being a light and easily handled material, greater lengths of mono- than multifilament netting can be accommodated in a fishing boat.

The mesh size used by drift netters has been described as very much a matter of choice, but varying between 2.5 and 3 in (6.4 to 7.6 cm) as measured from knot to knot in the netting. These nets are size selective and a mesh of these dimensions is believed to retain salmon of between 3 and 8 lb in weight (1.4 to 3.6 kg). Sea trout are an incidental or by-catch. A survey of almost 2,000 sea trout taken by drift net off the south-west coast revealed that the smallest was 3.1 lb (1.4 kg) and the overall average weight of the sample was 4.6 lb (2.1 kg).

Because 90 per cent of the relatively slim Atlantic-feeding and 50 per cent of the Irish Sea-feeding trout of over 4 lb (1.8 kg) have spawned at least once, the sea trout most likely to be caught in a salmon drift net may be regarded as a previous spawner. The salmon drift net catch is relatively small along the eastern seaboard and the most extensive drift net fisheries occur off the southern and western parts of the coast where Atlantic-feeding trout predominate. Thus when the vulnerability of sea trout to this form of capture is considered a comment on the occurrence of previously spawned fish in the stocks is apposite.

With the single exception of the Waterville fishery in Co. Kerry, Irish sea trout stocks are short-lived and consequently their average weight is low and the number of previous spawners in the stocks is small. It has been estimated that the number of previous spawners within the Connemara stocks is probably in the vicinity of 4 per cent while an investigation of the Moy fishery revealed the figure was as low as 2 per cent. These facts suggest that there are few sea trout in Ireland of sufficiently large size to be captured by salmon drift nets and further details support the unlikelihood of a large proportion of sea trout landings deriving from these engines.

Sea trout run into freshwater in a sequence of descending size which can be related to feeding activity. The largest pre-spawned and previously spawned fish enter in the early spring at a time when drift netters, although entitled to fish, do not do so in large numbers. Because of the relatively small size of post-smolts remaining at sea during the summer months when drift netters are most active, these trout, which are too small to mesh, are largely unaffected by the nets. The sea trout of the Currane fishery in Co. Kerry were found to contain as large a proportion of previous spawners in the mid 1970s as during the early 1940s when similar population description work was carried out, so that the effects of recent drift netting are not obvious in that stock. During the earlier years of the official statistics the proportion of sea trout landings attributed to drift nets averaged at 3 per cent by weight but this figure is likely to have increased with the more widespread use of these nets.

Drift nets with a smaller mesh size are used locally for the capture of sea trout on the east coast.

Draft nets

Draft or seine nets are operated by encircling fish which do not strike the net although some of the smaller individuals may mesh in the netting. Draft nets are usually 100 yds (91 m) in length but there are local variations. The net is set by boat, one end being held on shore while the remainder is paid out around a shoal of trout or salmon. The two ends of the net are then drawn up on a beach, stranding the fish that have been enclosed.

A variation on this technique known as 'looming' in the Wicklow draft net fishery on the east coast, is practised by setting the draft net in a semi-circle out from a beach. One end is drawn along by boat, the other by men on shore and the net moves thus some distance parallel to the strand before the ends are brought together and the net and contents beached. Looming is carried out during the hours of darkness.

The meshing of a draft net is often largest in the *wings* or end panels and reduces in size in the *bunt* or central portion which contains the fish. There are two mesh sizes in use: the ordinary statutory minimum of 1.75 in (4.5 cm) (knot to knot) permits post-smolt sea trout to get through although it can be manipulated deftly so that as the bunt nears the shore the centre meshes are stretched obliquely rather than full square. In the Lower River Feale (the River Cashen) in south-west Ireland this deft stranding of the net is known as the 'Ballyhorgan whip'. Alternatively, and illegally, a small-meshed net known as a *caitín* is stretched across the bunt and this retains the smaller post-smolts. The use of a small-meshed draft net is allowed by local by-law on parts of the eastern Irish coast. The by-laws stipulate a bunt mesh of 1 in (2.5 cm) (knot to knot). The small-meshed nets take mainly post-smolts and the larger, meshes retain fish of one sea winter.

Monthly characteristics of the sea trout catch were described from the draft net landings on the Lismore Estate which takes trout from the Rivers Blackwater and Bride in Co. Waterford. A catch in February was recorded only once in nineteen years reviewed and sea trout were rarely taken in April. Regular catches were recorded in May and as many fish were taken in this month as in August, but more than 90 per cent of the sea trout captured annually were taken by draft net in June and July. This fishery exploits short-lived sea trout stocks. The average weight of individual sea trout captured was very similar from one month to another. The lowest monthly average weight (in August) was 1.25 lb (0.57 kg) the highest (in April) 1.47 lb (0.67 kg). These were trout of mainly two sea summers (one sea winter) or, rather, fish which would have completed their second season of growth at sea.

According to official statistics for Ireland in all years prior to 1973 draft nets and rod and line accounted for, between them, more than 85 per cent and usually more than 90 per cent, of the annual sea trout landings. The exceptional years, 1973, 1976 and 1977, were due to a large proportion of the catch being attributed to drift nets. The number of draft net licences issued varied between a minimum of 589 in 1961 and 1962 to a maximum of 850 in 1950. The consequences for the draft net fishery of the growth of the drift net effort for salmon have been serious but the sea trout takings by draft net appear to have held up well.

Rod and line fisheries, variations on a theme

The sea trout angling season in Ireland is concentrated into the summer months, beginning with the influx of post-smolts from the sea in July (refer back to Fig. 33, to verify migrations). Catch statistics collected over long periods indicate that this pattern is widespread throughout the country and where biological assessments of the stocks have been carried out the short-lived nature of Irish sea trout emerges as a reason for it. There is only one long-lived Irish sea trout stock, that of the Currane fishery in Co. Kerry whose catch records, when compared with those of finnock fisheries, illustrate the range in season due to natural factors. Other catch frequency distributions can be attributed primarily to differences in angler behaviour.

Post-smolt or finnock fisheries

Anglers capture sea trout on migration from relatively rich marine feeding areas to the mainly soft water streams in which they spawn. Parr development there culminates in a spring migration of smolts and there is another exodus of juvenile fish which do not change to silver smolt livery in the autumn. These fish silver up in salt water and are assumed to start contributing to the sea trout stock the following year. A part of the spring smolt migration returns to fresh water after a brief sojourn at sea and this cohort, possibly augmented by fish which migrated for the first time as brown trout the previous autumn, is an important element in any sea trout fishery; in some Irish fisheries they are virtually the only exploitable fish.

Their first marine feeding period may last as few as two or three months and large numbers of finnock move inland if heavy rains coincide with the July spring tides. In fact the migration of this cohort has commenced some time previously. However the finnock season gets underway in July and is consequently brief. That part of Fig. 54 referring to post-smolt fisheries is compiled from more than 40,000 captures, recorded over a twenty year period in two Connemara fisheries.

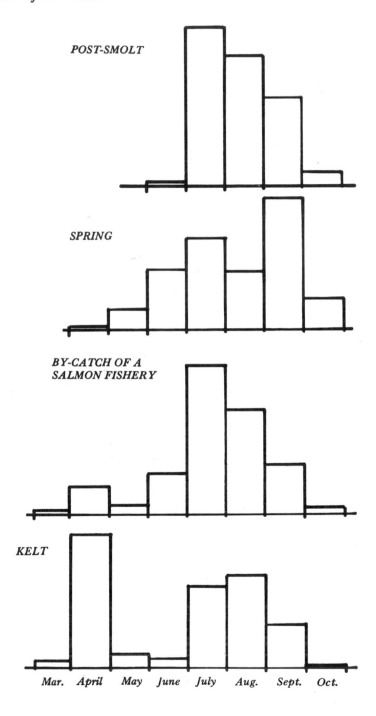

Fig. 54 Variations on a theme: the relative monthly distribution of catch in four types of sea trout fisheries. The terminology is as used in the text.

Spring fisheries

Among anglers there has been much debate as to the role played by finnock in subsequent migratons. In some parts of Ireland it is believed that these little fish never grow much larger and that heavier and older sea trout have a different life history. Several absence habits have been postulated but the extent to which any is adhered to is virtually impossible to demonstrate conclusively. Some sea trout spawn as finnock (that is in their first post-migration winter) while some finnock overwinter in freshwater without spawning. Hence the spring run to salt water can consist of a mixture of unspawned trout and kelts. The mending fish feed in the sea or estuary for a brief period before returning to inland waters when they are accompanied by the larger, unspawned sea trout.

Because larger trout move into fresh water in the spring months they comprise a run which is comparable in biological terms with that of spring salmon. A spring run occurs to some extent in all sea trout fisheries but it is significant only when the life expectancy of a stock is long and these fish are present in sufficient numbers to be attractive to anglers. The part of Fig. 54 referring to spring sea trout fisheries was compiled from data on almost 16,000 captures, taken in five years on the Currane fishery in Co. Kerry.

Spring sea trout fisheries have a longer angling season, beginning earlier in the year. But the larger fish which go torpid and stale after a brief stay in freshwater become active again towards the end of the season. The average weight of catch tends to rise then in both finnock and spring fisheries but the average weight of trout taken is relatively higher towards the end of the angling season in spring than in finnock fisheries.

Another difference between finnock and spring rod and line fisheries is to be found in the occurrence of undersized fish in the catch. All fish taken in May in a finnock fishery may be undersized but their incidence thereafter falls off. In a spring fishery however a large proportion of trout captured in May is acceptable.

By-catch of a salmon fishery

Where salmon are the main objective of the angler sea trout can be taken as a by-catch. Exactly why in some fisheries the emphasis should be on the pursuit of one species rather than the other is not known but in the example described here the fishery is quite small and presumably the anglers concerned have specific preferences. At first sight the frequency distribution of the catch throughout the year resembles that of a spring sea trout fishery. It lacks, however, the late summer large sea trout component. Examination of the average weight of the fish concerned confirms the fishery as a finnock producer. The effort expended on salmon angling in the earlier months of the year is rewarded with the capture of some of the early running sea trout. While these appear to make up a large proportion of the entire catch, it should be noted that the annual total is small. The histogram in Fig. 54 describing the by-catch of a salmon fishery is drawn from fewer than 600 captures recorded over a period of twenty-two years.

Kelt and recovering spent fisheries

Fishing for spent sea trout is illegal. Identifying these fish can however pose problems and they are sometimes captured by anglers. In a kelt fishery the summer catch is typically that of a finnock stock and there is neither the extension of the season in spring nor late summer that would be expected in a spring fishery. The Easter catch peak coincides with the downstream migration of kelts to salt water: examination of scales to confirm the identity of these fish may be necessary.

Sea trout are multiple spawners and can be considerably longer-lived than salmon; the effects of spawning would therefore seem to be less injurious to them than to the larger species of which only small numbers survive to spawn a second time. The Condition of trout which feed in the Irish Sea is better than that of sea trout whose marine feeding takes place in the Atlantic. Those fish which make up the majority of the anglers' catch are slim-bodied and even when freshly run in from the sea, frequently display the rather gaunt aspect of kelt sea trout. The histogram in Fig. 54 referring to kelt fisheries contains data on more than 3,000 captures, taken over a fifty-six year period in a Connemara fishery.

When fishing the mixture of ascending and descending trout which accumulate in sea loughs and the lower reaches of river systems in the spring and early summer months of the year, an angler is almost certain to encounter kelt sea trout sooner or later. Henry Lamond suggested that killing the fish need not be characterised as poaching. Thoughtlessness and ignorance usually lay at the root of such an offence. However when in the years prior to 1904 Lamond noted that every Saturday in February as many as 70 sea trout were reported as taken by anglers on the Leven, he considered it prudent to initiate a timely prosecution to end a form of sport which thereafter became very rare.

Yield in time

Angling memories abound in big fish and plenty of them. The truth, wherever it can be distilled from angling recollection, is not so impressive. We will seek it from two sources, one the well documented Connemara Fishery District, the other the official returns of angling catches from the anglers themselves.

Although Connemara has, for as long as official reports have been issued, been regarded as the leading or premier sea trout district in Ireland, its catch, to the more successful anglers (i.e. those who report their catches), is less than 2 lb (0.91 kg) of sea trout per rod day according to the official angling returns rather than the fishery registers maintained there. This represents approximately two fish per rod day. About 10,000 are taken by rod in the District annually. The total catch there and its average weight are both regarded as indicative of angling success for this form of trout on a national scale.

Within the Connemara Fishery District sea trout greatly outnumber and usually outweigh the salmon catch. Traditionally these sea trout have been regarded as an angler's rather than a commercial species and in recognition of this fact a by-law stipulates that drift nets should be of sufficiently large mesh size to avoid the capture of these fish which have a predominantly low weight and small size.

The Connemara catch is exceptionally well recorded; data for some fisheries go back to the mid nineteenth century. In the best documented catchments which together occupy some 50 per cent of the land surface of the Fishery District it is possible to attribute the majority of fish caught since 1900 to named captors. Catches in certain of the Connemara fisheries were depressed during the wars and this trend is obvious also in the official returns. It was during the same period that the draft net share of the national catch increased.

The number of sea trout returned by the District inspector in 1978 was 9,879 which, at an average weight of 0.75 lb (0.34 kg) would amount to a total of 7,400 lb (3,357 kg). The District fishery inspector in Connemara compiled his information from the totals captured in individual fisheries and these are probably something of an understatement of the true position although figures from this source are comparable from one year to the next.

The catch per unit effort (alternatively expressed as per rod per day) is a difficult statistic to interpret in Irish sport fisheries because of periodic alterations in the licensing system. In spite of this reservation the catch per licence displays a gradual decline until 1959 after which it stabilises, within the same range until the early seventies. The salmon catch per rod licence had been gradually declining prior to the increase in drift netting in the late 1960s, after which the share of the salmon catch to all engines other than drift nets fell off. Similar pre-1960 trends were demonstrated in the number of sea trout taken per rod day in Connemara.

A change in angler behaviour has been offered as the explanation for a decrease in yield per rod effort.

As this century advanced the number of angling licences sold annually greatly increased so that if the total catch remained the same the individual angler's share must have diminished. This theory is supported by several indicators of angling success. In the Connemara District for instance the number of trout reportedly caught per licence sold has tended downwards for as long as figures have been collected. In that District also the number of sea trout taken per rod day has also declined. These two statistics (number of trout caught per licence sold and number of sea trout caught per rod day) are however expressed in different terms which cannot be reconciled with each other because of periodic changes in the licensing system. In other words it is not feasible to demonstrate that one 'licence unit' in Connemara is equivalent to so many 'rod days'.

Even if the individual angler's share of the landings has declined there is no reason why the proficient fisherman cannot make a spectacularly better than average bag. Angling journals tend to spotlight these; beside them the cold statistical truth is less than dramatic. Anglers too have a happy knack of remembering the good days which, as time goes by, come to be regarded as the norm. Nationally the average reward for a day's sea trout fishing in Ireland is less than 1 lb (0.45 kg) of fish. In the earlier decades of this century it was higher and the average of 1 lb was established in the early 1960s when it accompanied a new pattern of tourism. It should be understood that an overall national figure of this kind obscures the fact that some regions yield considerably more sea trout to the angler than others. Nor is the small reward a disincentive; just under one-third of all (licensed) angling days are currently devoted to sea trout.

Translated into numbers a bag weight of 1 lb of sea trout per day represents roughly one fish. There are important exceptions to this rule, notably the Currane fishery in Co. Kerry, where the average weight at capture can be as high as 1.8 lb (0.82 kg) over a season but it is the slight fluctuations over and below the 1 lb national average from one year to another which are particularly significant. Sea trout are not produced at a constant rate in freshwater. Instead there are good years, usually associated with mild weather, when the output of juveniles to the sea is high. These young trout feed in inshore marine waters and many return, sometimes after an absence of only weeks, to the rivers and lakes which produced them. A good finnock year results in a lower individual catch weight and this characteristic is discernible in a particular year in fisheries as far apart as Kerry and Donegal. In the early and middle years of the 1970s sea trout production in freshwater was high but has since declined. The yield to the angler has not fluctuated accordingly, a fact which supports the belief that angler enthusiasm has at least as great an influence on the performance of these fisheries as natural factors.

13

Record Keeping, Record Fish

The fisherman who keeps a diary stores memories to be revisited with pleasure but the fishery manager who logs his catches compiles a valuable data bank.

Previous pages have shown how the records can be interpreted. Over a period of years the monthly catch distribution and the average weights of the individual fish characterise the type of stock and fishery. Variation in the average catch weight from one year to another can also be an indicator of the age composition of the stocks, but great caution and additional information may be required to interpret this. A lower than average catch weight in a certain year could mean that a large proportion of the yield was post-smolts, that the exodus from freshwater of smolts was large and that the stocks were expanding. Or it might simply indicate that intercepting gill nets were sieving the larger fish out of the incoming run.

If one ignores the local and sporadic incidents of poaching and pollution, salmonid production and output from freshwater displays certain general characteristics over a wide area and consideration of fishery records from different places may give an accurate picture of the state of the stocks.

As far as anglers are concerned there are two very different approaches to their sport. Competitive match angling for cyprinid or coarse fish species requires large numbers of fish which may individually be very small. The game fisherman is also content with a large bag which individually, though larger than those acceptable to the match angler, may not be very spectacular. For the game fisherman the occasional big fish makes the season.

Depending on where one is fishing big sea trout may be variously defined and always in terms of their rarity. Where rich sea feeding and long-lived fish coincide, as on the Welsh coast, trout of 10 to 15 lb (4.5 to 6.8 kg) are fairly frequent. In Connemara the combination of short life and poor feeding make a sea trout of 3 lb (1.4 kg) a good one. The coincidence of long life and poor feeding on the Atlantic coast make a trout of 5 to 6 lb (2.3 to 2.7 kg) a noteworthy catch.

Catch registers dating from the early years of the century were laid out in several headed columns. *Date*, *Name of Fisherman* and *Comments* on angling conditions were usually printed in these registers. There were separate spaces for the numbers and bag weights of salmon, sea trout and sometimes brown trout. Occasionally an extra column requested details of the best individual weight of the day.

It is regrettable that this last column did not instead specify the number of sea trout equalling or exceeding a certain weight threshold. The threshold could be as low as 3 lb (1.4 kg) in a post-smolt fishery and as heavy as 10 lb (4.5 kg) in a fishery exploiting an Irish Sea feeding spring running population. Such a record would very likely be a highly informative account of fluctuations in the stocks.

In Chapter 5 we saw that sea trout are produced in freshwater in numbers which depend on growing conditions. Favourable growing seasons tend to occur in clusters in accordance with variation in sun spot numbers. From their moment of birth the fish begin to die and the decline in numbers of those fish which hatched in a particular year is time-dependent. For instance, if there are 200 sea trout in year one and if 50 per cent die annually, by year two there will be 100 which will further reduce to 50 by year three and to 25 by year four. If, instead, there were 2,000 fish in year one, there would be 1,000 in year two, 500 in year three and 250 in year four.

If effective angling effort is fairly constant and the total yield of fish is fairly stable — and this would seem to be the case — then the occasionally larger number of heavier fish should register in the records, indicating a large post-smolt exodus some years previously. The anglers' catch may be recorded but the smolt exodus will almost certainly not be.

The kind of information tabulated under *Heaviest fish* is not amenable to this kind of analysis so there is little opportunity to test the hypothesis on the majority of angling registers.

There is however one source of data to be consulted. In 1955 the Irish Specimen Fish Committee instituted a scheme to collect on a national scale records of the incidence of heavy rod caught fish of a range of species, dubbed 'specimen' fish. For sea trout the qualifying weight was initially 7 lb (3.2 kg) but this weight proved so elusive that within a couple of years it was re-set at 6 lb (2.7 kg).

The Irish Specimen Fish scheme might be regarded as an angling log in macrocosm. In the thirty years of its existence the number of large sea trout recorded annually has fluctuated between none and fourteen in a very definite pattern (Fig. 55). The sea trout which have been reported under the scheme occur in four aggregations. Before going into the significance of these it would be worthwhile to consider the nature of these large fish.

From each specimen trout scales are removed to confirm that the fish is sea-run and these can be used to age the individual. The freshwater or parr age of the majority is two years and there is little B-type growth. In other words, most of these specimens are fast freshwater growers

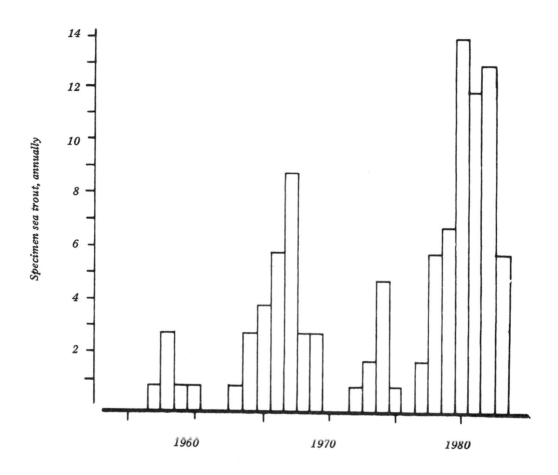

*Fig. 55   Recorded occurrence of large or 'specimen' sea trout
in Ireland from 1955 to 1983 inclusive.*

which migrate to sea for the first time early in the year. They do not
dally in an estuary nor do they leave the river late in the spring.

Because of their young smolt age, these trout commence sea growth
at a young age. Thus, it can be said of their life, that a higher than usual
proportion is devoted to making flesh in the sea. This is a significant point
because a sea trout of a given age has a number of alternatives when
allocating its time between freshwater and marine conditions. Either choice
has consequences for the weight of the fish as can be shown by reference
to actual aged examples from the Currane fishery. All of the following
have a total (i.e. a marine plus freshwater) age of four years:

| Age | | Weight | |
Freshwater	Marine	lb	kg
4.	.0	0.69	0.31
3.	.1	1.75	0.79
2.	.2	2.30	1.04

If therefore a fish has a certain allotted span, the earlier it descends to sea, the heavier it will weigh at the end of it. If the growing conditions which accompany its parr phase encourage rapid development and, in addition, militate in favour of a larger smolt exodus, at a later time there will be an increased incidence of heavier than usual sea run fish.

Specimen sea trout have been produced in Ireland apparently in accordance with this formula. The fish have an average age of seven to eight years and their brief parr life has enabled them to achieve qualifying weight within it.

Clusters of specimen sea trout are a genuine reflection of abundance rather than a consequence of sporadically greater angling effort. It can also be shown from their scales that specimen fish passed their parr years in favourable growing conditions.

A minority of specimen sea trout come from the Irish Sea and these are of relatively young sea age because their faster growth and better Condition enable them to reach qualifying weight at a younger total age. The majority of Atlantic-feeding trout come from the Currane fishery in Co. Kerry whose fish have a propensity for long life. Occasionally specimen fish are captured in other freshwater systems draining into the Atlantic but these are few in number. A lower qualifying weight might well demonstrate the cyclical occurrence of sea trout production by short-lived stocks, even those exploited as post-smolts.

14

Shifting Perspectives on Changing Circumstances

Perhaps the most catastrophic threat to sea trout fisheries is the spread of acid rain. It arises from the burning of fossil fuels in the course of which sulphurous gases are released to the atmosphere where they mix with water vapour and return to earth as a potent biocide. Acid rain is not lethal to sea trout alone, so it is not considered here in depth. Any fish species which has a freshwater life on calcium-poor rocks is vulnerable to it.

If acid rain has the greatest potential for the most widespread destruction, more conventional forms of pollution are not abating and excessive fishing is intensifying. To safeguard sea trout a ready and convenient means of assessing its state of health is required. There are methods of automatically counting migratory salmonids, but the installation of requisite equipment is costly and largely confined to a small number of valuable salmon-bearing waters. One turns then to the beneficiaries of sea trout to canvass their opinions on the immediate state of the resource. After all they are the people who have most intimate contact with the fish. There is some justification for regarding anglers rather than commercial fishermen as taking most sea trout; they are not slow in putting forward their views — which are influential. They recommend innovations in conservation and stock improvement, they promote changes in the law and they produce the greater part of the most digestible literature on the fish. But how reliable are their opinions?

Numbers of sea trout available to anglers wax and wane in the medium term, in response to natural regulators such as climate and to human activities such as heavy fishing and pollution, but its biology contributes towards a steady supply of fish to the angler. With this as a backdrop let us examine some commentaries in the literature on the state of sea trout stocks.

William Makepeace Thackeray was quite ecstatic about angling prospects in Connemara. In 1902 he wrote:

> O you, who laboriously throw flies into English rivers, and catch at the expiration of a hard day's walking, casting and wading, two or three feeble little brown trouts of two or three ounces in weight, how would you rejoice to have but an hour's sport in Derryclear or

> Ballinahinch; where you have but to cast and lo! a big trout springs at your fly . . .

Oscar Wilde in the 1870s wrote in correspondence of his satisfaction with the Lough Fee system, also in Connemara, where the yield of sea trout to the rod was a steady four fish per day.

Wilde and Thackeray were two observers who appeared satisfied with the resource. Perhaps they were not so emotionally involved with the sport as the committed and enthusiastic anglers who provide most documentation about this fish. The anxiety to protect cultivates expectations of decline. Or perhaps it is a quirk of angling memories that the better days are in the past. That kind of comment can be attributed to all but a few of the most influential commentators who have a certain unanimity of approach — regretting the deterioration of the resource. In the Irish context Kingsmill Moore was happy with the situation he had observed in the Connemara fisheries but J.P. Digby was adamant about a decline in the size of catch and a general disimprovement in some of the angling lakes which he claimed were no longer worth fishing in 1951.

As the great bulk of the sea trout angling literature refers to Scotland, it is to commentators there that reference must be made to examine the nature of the concern expressed.

Hamish Stuart observed:

> The sadly significant fact (is) that the numbers of sea trout in many waters which held this, the most sporting of the Salmonidae in great abundance is steadily decreasing . . .

Henry Lamond commented that sea trout had never enjoyed more than a precarious existence for reasons which are plausible enough; being a summer running fish it had suffered from the cumulative effects of pollution, he suggested, and its spawning grounds had become greatly curtailed. The fact that the fish chose small streams in which to spawn meant they were more vulnerable to drought than salmon.

Sidney Spencer recognised the fluctuating nature of the sea trout run:

> In some years a run will fail to appear and anglers throughout the river system will speculate as to why. Sometimes very occasionally it is possible to pinpoint the answer — a bad spawning season — shortage of spawners — an untimely flood plus frost or the like the appropriate number of seasons previously in the case of salmon — or perhaps sheer lack of water. In the latter case the fish may have fallen victim to estuary nets — or they may have run late — too late for angling observation.

Being a sporting rather than a commercial fish the majority of observations on the abundance of sea trout have been made by anglers rather than netsmen.

Several aspects of angling operations colour dispassionate appraisal of whatever facts one could glean about such a moody prey. In addition to the variation in the suitability of angling conditions resulting from hot and dry or wet fishing seasons which, apart from influencing the availability of the fish, may impose restrictions on angling efficiency, other factors which may have consequences for the sea trout yield would include variations in angling enthusiasm.

In the early years of the century the average yield of sea trout in certain of the Connemara fisheries, calculated from their angling registers and estimated on an annual basis, varied between four and eight sea trout per day. This statistic tended downwards until in the 1960s it stabilised and has remained at approximately one fish per day since. The most ready explanation for this alteration in yield is a change in angler behaviour. During the early years of the century Connemara offered a visitor little alternative to fishing. By the early 1960s communications within the region had greatly improved, more leisure amenities were provided and anglers, many of whom visited in family groups, availed of facilities other than angling.

Another imponderable is the change in angling methods — a continuous development.

Henry Lamond recalled in 1932, the occasion on which he met R.A. Chrystal who

> had one sea trout of 2 lb caught with a salmon fly whose nose was decorated with a revolving spinner, the kind of thing one sees in coloured plates in tackle makers catalogues, but, in my experience, seldom elsewhere.

It is probably true to say that in the majority of sea trout fisheries spinning is regarded as an inferior form of sport. However being a relatively straightforward and mechanical exercise, requiring less skill than fly fishing, records of sea trout yield to spinning would possibly be a better indication of stock abundance. Instead anglers base their impressions on fly caught fish although the nature of this pursuit has changed considerably over the years. Two aspects of this deserve consideration here, changes in the size and the pattern of fly.

Although anglers frequently comment on the quality of the sport and from these observations deduce changes in the abundance of the fish, angling methods change with fashionable influence. Hugh Falkus referred to the fact that: 'Few fishermen can resist filling their cases with flies . . .' and virtually every commentator prescribes a different list of patterns. Among these the teal winged flies like the Peter ross usually find a mention as occasionally do the Butcher, Claret and mallard and Black pennell. Having faith in your fly is half the battle advised Richard Clapham and he went on to recommend that pattern is less important than size. But most angling writers have something to say on the latter and there has been a decided shift in ideas over the years.

Sidney Spencer said, in the late 1960s, if one consulted the illustrated books on the sport at the beginning of the century one would find sizes and shapes of flies which 'look ludicrous today'. The tendency he perceived was a reduction in the size of lure in response to a greater discrimination by the fish. The explanation for adopting smaller flies was to be found in smaller runs of fish, a bag of which demanded more precise angling skills. However, Spencer observed that the tendency towards the use of smaller flies was not growing as fast as he thought it should.

Hamish Stuart recollected that the typical Loch Lomond flies of his earliest experience were much larger than those later in use. He also felt that sea trout had responded to the general adoption of smaller flies. Experience, he suggested, seemed to justify the view that sea trout had become a more fastidious fish in the matter of flies over a period of fifty years. Henry Lamond on the other hand expressed a view that the large and rough fly was more appropriate to sea trout because it had a prototype in nature and Hugh Falkus has also stated that larger flies are more successful:

> Sea trout will accept a variety of shapes and sizes of lure and I am in no doubt whatsoever that the flies most commonly used for sea trout fishing are much too small . . . I will go so far as to suggest to any sea trout fisherman . . . that if he doubles the size of his fly he will go a long way towards doubling the size of his bag . . .

If angling methods vary as they evidently have done, can the yield to the rod be equated with effort to catch the fish over the longer term?

The several studies available on the food of the sea trout show it to be largely piscivorous when in the sea. A wide range of other organisms, notable among them various species of Crustacea, are also consumed in the sea and estuary. Once sea trout return to fresh water their feeding becomes intermittent, but fish still feature among their prey along with representatives of many of the major freshwater invertebrate taxa. In general sea trout are fairly omnivorous so it is of interest to review the lures and fly patterns employed to catch them in fresh water.

Just how representative these are of the prey of sea trout has provoked much discussion in the past and it will quite possibly remain a subject for conjecture always. One thing is however certain: the flies used in sea trout angling are known to have changed considerably in the past.

As part of its contribution to the Cork International Exhibition the Irish Department of Agriculture and Technical Instruction prepared a collection of fishing flies and published a catalogue of them in 1902. The flies were obtained on the advice of experienced anglers in each of the twenty-four fishing districts into which the island was divided at the time and they were supplied by recommended makers. Details of the effective period for each pattern were also given. The collection provides a fascinating and often bewildering array of material and the Preface to the Catalogue carries a cautionary note that flies 'known by the same name, are often very differently dressed in different districts'.

In all, thirty-seven waters or groups of waters were listed as containing sea trout and for these a total of some 180 fly labels were recommended, making an average of almost five dressings per fishery. In fact very few of the named patterns were widespread and examples of the few that were displayed considerable variation. So, the Fiery brown, listed as effective in sixteen fisheries, was made up of very different materials dressed in distinctive patterns in all of them.

Next most popular patterns were the Zulu, from ten fisheries, and the Golden olive and Orange grouse dressings, each recorded from eight waters, ranging between Co. Derry and Co. Kerry. The Claret was recommended on seven fisheries but additional variants of it were collected from others and the Blue doctor, Thunder and lightning and three other dressings were each used in five different systems. Only two further patterns were employed on four fisheries and seven flies were said to be effective on three, so the majority of labels came from one or two fisheries only.

When these patterns were classified into groupings the majority could not be related to known invertebrates but there were a number (Black spider, Yellow sally, Black quill and Blue bottle) which corresponded with likely prey. In all 23 Ephemeropteran (mayfly) patterns, the Alder, three Plecopteran (stonefly) and seven terrestrial Dipteran (fly) dressings, a beetle imitation, the cuckoo spit (Wren's tail) and a general spider pattern were identified and accounted for about 20 per cent of the patterns classified.

The olive patterns are, as a group, recommended for use throughout the fishing season and when, as happens, imitations of *Baetis rhodani*, one of the commonest species, are said in the Catalogue to be effective all season in one catchment and only during August in another, it must be assumed that more attractive prey displace it at certain times and under special conditions. An alternative conclusion might be that the killing qualities of the various patterns have not been accurately compared.

With little agreement from one system to another as to which fly patterns were of general use and on the dates on or within which the more generally distributed ties kill, it is apposite to note that the majority of rivers frequented by sea trout have many characteristics in common. Among these is an invertebrate community (the food supply) which is widespread and which presents little regional variation in its common component species. Where investigations have been undertaken on the life histories of invertebrates frequenting sea trout producing streams, few regional differences among them have been reported. All of which makes variations in the reported killing period and the discontinuous distribution of certain natural imitations the more difficult to understand.

About one quarter of the flies catalogued could be described as sedges or sedge-like patterns (caddis flies) and many of these were described on their labels as Rails, Grey flags and Silverthorns. A slightly smaller proportion of the patterns was of drab wet flies, possibly representative of indeterminate arthropods. Such flies as the Claret series could be classified under 'indeterminate' because they can be described as 'nymph suggesting' patterns. In this sub-division could also be placed the Palmer and Bumble flies which are thought to represent a range of arthropods originating in terrestrial or aquatic surroundings.

Finally there are the gaudy fancy ties, representative of what is sometimes described as a 'sea-memory' because they cannot be said to resemble known freshwater prey. About 30 per cent of the patterns fell into this category.

A curious feature of the geographical occurrence of the various patterns was a tendency for one of the broader groupings listed above to predominate in certain regions. In one of the Connemara fisheries for example, about 60 per cent of the patterns used were classified as 'sea-memory' flies and to neighbouring waters were attributed a large proportion of dressings of this kind. Further south, in the Kerry fisheries, on the other hand, the more drab and natural imitations predominated.

It should be said that in some of the Kerry fisheries brown were given with sea trout as the fisherman's quarry whereas that is not true of the Connemara waters in which salmon are occasionally mentioned as an alternative. However, this does not apply to every fishery in either region so that there is a strong possibility that the distinctive lines of evolution in fly tying owe more to the imagination of angling man than to the dietary preferences of sea trout.

To summarise, if one were to accept the fly tyings of the Cork collection as representative of sea trout predilections in food, the fish would have very varied and specific tastes from one river system to the next. This is not merely unlikely, it does not correspond with the known foods of the fish in fresh water before migration. The patterns concerned bear no resemblance to the known marine diet and the returning fish is not usually an enthusiastic feeder. So, the very modern trend towards few fly patterns is probably the most sensible approach. But man lives not by science but according to the dictates of myth and having confidence in one's methods is everything. Against such a background of inconstant technique — if one can regard angling as a sampling method — could one accord credence to the catch as an indicator of the strength of the stocks?

15

Tradition and Dogma

Sea trout are not sufficiently valuable to justify the kind of high technological surveillance expended on some commercial fish species. For them the angling lobby holds a watching brief. Its pronouncements may not be always very accurate but they err on the pessimistic side, they counsel caution and are ever mindful of the fragile nature of the resource. Their traditions and rules may be dogma solidified by repetition but they have the virtue of stable yields of the fish over a period of more than one hundred years. How thoroughly and obediently such regulations have been observed in that time is anyone's guess. Their efficacy has never been critically examined; they are articles of faith rather than established fact.

For sea trout many of the management procedures and techniques are similar to those employed for other game species such as Atlantic salmon and brown trout. They involve keeping spawning gravels in good condition, constructing engineering works on streams and general protection of broodstock. Two issues are of particular relevance to sea trout and both are referred to by virtually all writers who recommend practical conservation measures for the fish. Almost every author on sea trout subscribes to size limits as a desirable conservation measure, the absence of which is likely to have serious consequences for the stocks. Some also describe artificial propagation of sea trout by hatcheries as a useful management technique. Whereas the first of these topics may not have serious implications if not observed, the second has a real destructive potential which daily becomes more apparent as information accrues on it.

Hatcheries and sea trout enhancement

Although the artificial propagation of salmonids has been practised since the eighteenth century it has come in for increasing scrutiny and criticism in recent years and is no longer regarded as an automatic first choice of technique for stock enhancement. At both the scientific and popular levels the movement and intermixture of broodstock is thought to have caused loss of genetic diversity and its benefits are questionable. Most effort in artificial propagation has been directed at Atlantic salmon; sea trout have received very little attention. In fact sea trout have been reared for as long though not so abundantly as the larger species.

Hatchery rearing techniques are used to supplement and augment wild salmonid stocks as well as for fish farming. Sea trout have not as yet been farmed, but there is some interest in farming brook trout *Salvelinus fontinalis* which, in many aspects of its life history, is identical to sea trout. The immediate question is whether artificial rearing techniques which have been widely used in game fisheries can benefit sea trout and where deficiencies are likely to occur in their operation.

In Ireland sea trout have been artificially propagated over a wide area for more than a century though in small numbers. Greatest effort was concentrated into the early years of this century when attempts were made to rear these fish in catchments, some of them far from the sea, which do not produce sea trout naturally.

If the above can be taken to indicate a haphazard approach to the propagation of this fish, the numbers of sea trout reared artificially were not great and fell very far behind those of salmon and brown trout. It is likely that the culture of sea trout was never very enthusiastically pursued; instead, because the techniques and requisite apparatus are similar to those used for salmon rearing, some sea trout culture was an incidental by-product of managing salmon. As for salmon the disposal of sea trout hatchery produce could take place at various stages; as eggs, unfed fry, yearlings or smolts, and the bulk of the material was probably distributed at the earlier of these. Hence information on the success of culturing the later stages of sea trout in Ireland still remains to be obtained.

Occasionally a note on the progress of sea trout propagation was published in the annual reports of the government department responsible for fisheries. The 1898 Report of the Inspectors of Irish Fisheries contained one such from a H.R. Laing describing the rearing of these fish in the Costelloe Hatchery in Connemara, a part of which is worthwhile examining in detail:

> . . . I hoped last year to see from my previous three years' sea trout hatching a marked increase of small July sea trout; but, on the contrary, there was a great falling off (we caught only half the quantity on the rod) . . .

This brief statement touches on three elements which complicate the evaluation of sea trout propagation. First is the difficulty of ascertaining in a sport fishery the strength of stocks from level of catches. Secondly, there is the homing behaviour of the fish. Sea trout are specific to their stream of origin when they reach maturity. Before that however sea trout dash in and out of freshwater systems irrespective of their provenance. The majority of sea trout in Ireland are exploited as post-smolts and there is a strong likelihood that these fish benefit catchments other than those in which they were reared. Artificial propagation, if it is to be successful at all in such circumstances, would have to operate on a regional rather than a single catchment basis. Finally, the natural fluctuations in a sea trout stock resulting from climatic changes can be sufficient to minimise or render superfluous any hatchery effort.

Artificial propagation is thought to serve a useful purpose where a salmonid has been reduced or eliminated. The circumstances in which this can occur vary from widespread pollution to persistent destruction of stocks by overfishing. On the other hand Henry Lamond commented:

> In the event of the stock of any of our greater salmon rivers becoming depleted from the effects of pollution, over-netting, poaching or some other known cause or causes, I would not, where the spawning grounds are adequate, attempt to restore or enhance the stock by the establishment of a hatchery. It is extremely doubtful if even very extensive, and therefore proportionately costly, hatchery operations would maintain the stock in face of continuing and possibly increasing evils. In the circumstances supposed expenditure would most economically be devoted to attacking the evil, for, if it were once removed, or minimised, nature would speedily restore the stock without adventitious aid.

Lamond did however anticipate a useful role for sea trout hatcheries when, in the event of a dry summer, the stocks are depleted by the vicissitudes of weather. Sea trout are supposed to be at greater risk than salmon because they spawn in smaller streams, frequent pools rather than riffles and are thus more vulnerable to being stranded by falling water levels, although some scientists have observed that they are rarely trapped when streams dry up. If drought is a hazard, the successful contribution of a hatchery would require that water shortage be anticipated some two or three years ahead. Another circumstance which would benefit, in theory, from the introduction of hatchery reared sea trout is where the fish had not previously existed and is to be established.

Places in which this generally occurs are above obstacles like impassable falls which, once removed, open new spawning territory to incoming fish. It should be borne in mind that impassable falls fulfil an important function in safeguarding genetic resources which are an important component of long-lived and hence the most valuable of sea trout stocks. In the case of sea trout, if the system contains them already it would be prudent to await their migration further upstream. Failing this the ova and milt of fish from the same system might be transplanted further upriver, provided the distance does not exceed the natural range of the fish.

Sea trout might be artificially propagated to maintain a stock for exploitation in an intensive put-and-take fishery. Whereas this practice is in general use for brown trout, sea trout which have a high mortality at sea and a protracted return pattern, are a more unsatisfactory subject. Additionally, sea trout achieve greater pre-migratory dimensions than salmon, necessitating a greater food input. They also make less weight at sea so that their rearing is more costly and their capture is a financially less rewarding exercise.

In recent years the validity of certain forms of trout accorded species and race status in the nineteenth century, has been confirmed and every stream population of *Salmo trutta* so far examined seems to possess distinctive genetic characteristics. Specific spawning strategies may have been developed to maintain genetic integrity. In this context hatchery crosses must be a relatively crude exercise. Investigation of the consequences of inbreeding in hatchery stocks of brown trout confirmed this and recommendations have been made to the effect that no stock should be founded or perpetuated using less than approximately thirty parents of the less numerous sex in any generation. Being a by-product of salmon propagation, hatchery rearing of sea trout has often been conducted on less rigorous lines.

Distinctive characteristics of importance to sea trout for which there is evidence of a genetic control include:

Longevity: The only long-lived stock in Ireland occurs in the Waterville Fishery. A dozen or so stocks of this kind are known in Britain and Ireland.

Fecundity: Short-lived sea trout stocks may have a tendency towards earlier maturation.

Homing behaviour: Specific stocks have capabilities to exploit inshore coastal or deeper waters more effectively.

The present exploitation of sea-run *S. trutta* is mainly in wild sport fisheries and this is also its foreseeable future. The use of artificially propagated sea trout to supplement natural shortfalls in production is not considered viable. Nor is re-stocking on a put-and-take basis. One of the few exceptional circumstances might be where a widespread and persistent environmental contamination occurs. Even then however a natural immigration and regeneration of the stocks would be the desirable means of achieving recovery.

Size limits

By law every angler is obliged to respect smolts which are defined by size and livery. These fish feed voraciously while on migration and so are vulnerable to anglers for that reason. The main culprits taking the little fish in large numbers at any time are probably juvenile anglers.

The size limits prescribed for smolts may extend protection to some of the smaller post-smolts because there is, as we have seen, some variation in length at any stage of the life cycle. Smolts are simply too small to make a worthwhile dish and this is probably one of the anglers' reasons for freeing them. The scientific rationale is the damage a heavy bag of smolts would inflict on the stocks. This reasoning could be extended to the incoming post-smolts and specific fishery regulations are formulated to protect both these and the larger smolts. Records of rejected fish are seldom kept but one of these from the Crumlin Fishery in Connemara for the years from 1897 to 1904 has details of silvered trout returned to the water. The size limit in force in the fishery was 12 in (30 cm) and, like all the Connemara fisheries, Crumlin has a post-smolt pattern of exploitation. In May all of the fish captured over the period for which these figures refer, were less than the prescribed size limit. In June 50 per cent were rejected; 18 to 20 per cent were returned to the water from July to September inclusive and in October 9 per cent were sub-size. Ironically parr (technically pre-smolts) were not protected nearly so thoroughly although trout may go seawards in this livery. In fact at times the removal of small brownies was recommended on the grounds that they competed with sea trout!

Thus we have a legal protection for smolts, fishery regulations for larger smolts and smaller post-smolts and for post-smolts, angling tradition. Whether these small fish should be retained by anglers has for long been a controversial matter and angling writers have presented strong and fairly united arguments in favour of their being freed. It is a debate which, because of the imprecise nature of the subject, has been dominated by the angler rather than the scientist.

H.P. Henzell made no bones about the fact that he 'had a bee in his bonnet' about the need for finnock conservation and he wished 'it to go out and sting every sea trout angler so that he could think and do likewise'.

The feeding habits of sea trout become more salmon-like as the fish grow and during their early returns to freshwater the post-smolts occasionally feed quite enthusiastically if the environmental conditions favour their doing so. In such circumstances they are vulnerable to mass slaughter and the majority of angling writers have alluded to instances of large bags resulting from relatively little fishing effort. Hamish Stuart recounts three rods taking two hundred herling on the worm at a single fishing. Sidney Spencer reported immense numbers of seven or eight ounce (200 to 225 g) fish being taken, especially in Scotland, 'to the measureless detriment of sea trout stocks'. And H.P. Henzell described it as a sickening sight to see, in the evening in some hotels, trays of fish containing perhaps eight or ten sizeable trout and forty or more finnock.

Virtually the entire angling lobby in Scotland preferred to allude to finnock in such terminology as R.A. Chrystal's 'Breakfast fish . . . not counted by most anglers but sometimes brought home for eating.' Hamish Stuart also, while not wholeheartedly in favour of a complete ban, suggested moderation in taking these fish: '. . . I always return herling unless I wish one or two for the table owing to the delicate character of their flesh.' Among angling writers Henry Lamond put forward a minority view:

> Sea trout in the whitling stage of their growth give the chief sport in the lower reaches (of the Leven). It has often been proposed to veto the capture of these immature fish, but this, in my opinion, under present conditions, would involve an unnecessary deprivation which would not be compensated for by any very certain advantage.

The prevailing recorded Scottish feeling — although it did not find favour in Ireland where the short-lived nature of sea trout stocks has meant that finnock comprise at least a sizeable minority of the rod catch — was expressed by W.J.M. Menzies:

> A feeling exists at least in certain districts, if not everywhere, for a size limit, either voluntary or statutory, below which sea trout can not be taken by rod and line.

Hamish Stuart made a similar recommendation but felt that a bag limit would be desirable also. Sidney Spencer stated that size was the only practical waterside guide. Henzell felt a size limit of 15 in (38 cm) should be enforced and Hugh Falkus advised this length as the demarcation between post-smolt and adult sea trout of one post-migration winter.

Hamish Stuart reckoned that the slaughter of finnock together with widespread poaching were the main reasons for the decline of sea trout. However one of the principal obstacles in assessing the consequences of finnock capture has been the difficulty of evaluating the significance of this phase of the sea trout life cycle. Menzies felt that without investigation we should not know whether whitling are the young stage of trout or a separate race. Henzell stated that he had been brought up on the principle that '. . . it is a good plan to cast your finnock on the waters and it will come back to you after many days as a fully fledged sea trout.' Any other suggestion that finnock might be a separate race or species he saw as '. . . an excuse for the retention by anglers of undersized fish'.

Fish size limits have been in operation for some two hundred years and several objectives for finnock protection have been given. Menzies advised that all fish species should have an opportunity of reproducing at least once before they are deliberately killed. Spencer also felt that the fish should have a chance to reproduce their young although he appreciated that about 80 per cent of finnock do not spawn. For this reason Menzies felt that sea trout older than post-smolt should be spared in some numbers (first maturation occurs in the first, second and third post-migration winter), although he regarded the imposition of a similar regulation for salmon as neither possible nor necessary.

Permitting a species to spawn once before death is undoubtedly a wise precautionary measure where its biology is not well known. In recent years there have been instances, where Atlantic salmon are heavily exploited, of a low density of juveniles in nursery streams. Where spawning salmonids occur in adequate numbers the tendency is for an over production of eggs which results in high mortalities during the first months of life due to intense competition for food. So, it is relatively easy to establish the effect of a size limit on egg production although it is more difficult to relate egg production to later stocks. Although the objective of adequate egg production is no longer so widely held or fashionable, it was at one time a general precautionary measure. The British Salmon and Freshwater Fisheries Act of 1923 prudently defined an immature fish as one 'of length less than such as may be prescribed by the by-laws'. And the formal expression of the purpose of these by-laws: 'Each fish must be given a chance to breed before it is killed.'

Hugh Falkus summarised the sea trout angler's ambitions in the following terms:

> Apart from herling, most of the sea trout we catch weigh between 1.5 (0.68) and 2.5 lb (1.13 kg). Anything over 3 lb (1.36 kg) is a good fish; anything in double figures the fish of a lifetime . . .

Some fishery scientists have stated that a bag limit, spreading effort evenly over stocks, rather than a size limit, might be the best way of achieving some larger fish. Irish 'specimen' sea trout derive mainly from young smolts which are produced in large numbers under certain favourable climatic conditions. Their rate of production is uneven and specimen sea trout occur in cycles some years after a heavy exodus to sea. As these cycles correspond with large seaward migrations the numbers of juveniles can be said to have a bearing on the number of large sea trout. In the same way the reduction of mortality at any stage in the life cycle, as by a diminution of angling effort, may have a beneficial outcome in larger numbers of heavy sea-run fish later.

One purpose of a size limit is to increase the maximum total weight of fish. In the case of sea trout it might be more accurate to describe the outcome as an improvement in the quality – though not the numbers caught. Describing the angling at Lochboisdale, South Uist, in 1939, R.A. Chrystal wrote:

> Lochboisdale fishings have a few peculiarities of their own, but they are all easily accounted for by one fact – that all the regular anglers are out for one thing i.e. big fish . . . Thus there is none of the murdering of finnock which disgraces many angling resorts . . . The due observance of the limit results in the overall catch averaging 2.5 to 2.75 lb (1.13 to 1.25 kg) per fish . . .

Menzies appreciated that finnock, on average, double their weight by the next season, which he considered a good reason for protecting the younger fish. Of course their numbers would also decline due to natural mortality in the intervening year. Spencer claimed to have close personal experience over many years of a fishery in which the catch of sea trout greater than 1 lb (0.45 kg) increased once the taking of finnock was prohibited. Unfortunately there are few well documented examples of such a size limit scheme in operation.

Although angling removes only a small proportion of the stock in a sea trout fishery (detailed counts from the Burrishoole Fishery in Co. Mayo suggest that proportions are in the region of 7 to 16 per cent of incoming fish) it does impose an extra mortality which, by taking some individuals at a small size, reduces the prospects for the stock increasing in weight. The purpose of returning post-smolts to the water — where it is practised — is to provide larger trout at a later stage.

The angling record of the Inver Fishery in Connemara from 1929 to 1974 (Fig. 56) is a detailed one which displays variation in catch numbers and in the average weight of landings. The Inver stock is a short-lived one which has a low weight at capture so the catch is mainly finnock. The Inver records suggest that when catches are high, the average weight of a sea trout taken is low and *vice versa*. From the data in Fig. 56 when the number of trout captured in a season is 500 their average weight is just below 1 lb (0.45 kg). Alternatively, when the

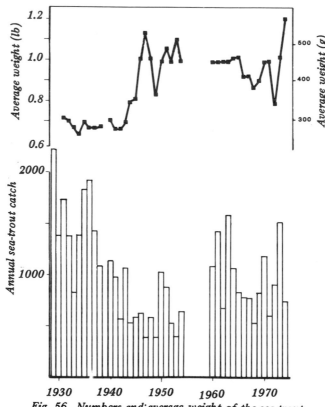

Fig. 56   Numbers and average weight of the sea trout
catch in the Inver Fishery (Connemara) between 1929
and 1974.

season's catch is 2,000 fish the average weight falls to below 0.75 lb (0.34 kg). Thus sufficient information is available here to support the contention that protecting a younger stage of sea trout produces a better quality of capture (a heavier weight of catch) some time later. Whether the actual reduction in numbers is adequately compensated by the quality of catch later is a value judgement to be made by the individual fishery manager.

Concerning sea trout size limits, as for so many other aspects of its biology which have a bearing on the way this fish is exploited, the facts which science elicits are not in themselves a solution to inadequate management. Their implications must be implemented and there are alternative ways of doing this. On the other hand, reliance on tradition, even when it has been tried and tested over a long period, is hardly a sensible way of conserving a valuable fish resource either. In a highly technological society whose wastes have the ability to destroy and whose ever more effective fishing techniques provide a means of overharvesting the fish, sea trout facts and figures are an indispensible ingredient in its conservation. Unfortunately that knowledge can also be employed to exploit the fish beyond its endurance.

If sea trout are to remain a valuable game and commercial fish something more than a factual basis for good management of them is required. That something has been provided to date by the angler and we can only hope his interest is sustained. It is appropriate then that the final word should be from an angler. Hamish Stuart, though writing in the early 1900s, anticipated much of the foregoing. His views were forthright and, although his reasoning was occasionally on unconventional lines, his instinct combined a distrust for omnipotent science with a respect for the fish. That must be the way ahead:

> The call in these days is naturally for facts and figures but it is to be feared that these facts and figures are sometimes as inadequate and misleading data as the oldest assumptions, and that they are often adapted to suit the purposes of those that use them with the objective of drawing convincing conclusions. There is at least no harm in expressing the pious wish that we shall not soon be robbed of the old joys of the speculative solution. Indeed, from some points of view, one dreads the advent of the day — if it ever dawns — on which the life history of Salmonidae will be as much a matter of commonplace knowledge as that of the barndoor fowl. Happily it can never be other than romantic. Long may the post prandial pipe furnish the swirling incense that lends an odour of sanctity to the wildest of speculative solutions offered at the day's end, when men discuss the immemorial problems of the fish and their ways! Let me add — and may my heresy be forgiven — that if I am a traitor to all modern thought, at least I glory in the sincerity of my treachery.

Appendix Table 1

Percentage age composition of two sea trout samples.
This Table provides details of Fig. 30.

Larger age grouping	Age category	Cummeragh	Moy
Sea years			
0	1. +	0.5	1.4
	2. +	34.6	51.9
	3. +	14.4	27.0
	4. +	0.9	1.1
1	1.1 +	0.7	1.8
	2.1 +	24.3	8.7
	3.1 +	3.5	1.9
	4.1 +	0.3	
	1. +S.M.+		0.1
	2. +S.M.+	0.3	3.2
	3. +S.M.+	0.6	1.7
	4. +S.M.+	0.3	
2	1.2 +	0.3	
	2.2 +	3.7	0.2
	3.2 +	0.3	
	4.2 +	0.1	
	1.1 +S.M.+	0.3	0.1
	2.1 +S.M.+	5.3	0.6
	3.1 +S.M.+	1.2	0.1
	4.1 +S.M.+	0.1	0.1
	1.2 S.M.+	0.2	
	2.2 S.M.+	3.1	0.2
	3.2 S.M.+	0.3	
	4.2 S.M.+	0.1	
3	2.3 +	0.2	
	2.3 S.M.+	0.3	
	3.2 +S.M.+	1.0	
	1.1 +2S.M.+	0.2	
	2.1 +2S.M.+	0.4	
	4.1 +2S.M.+	1.1	
4	2.1 +3S.M.+	0.2	
	2.2 +2S.M.+	0.6	
	2.3 +S.M.+	0.1	
5	2.1 +4S.M.+	0.1	
	3.1 +4S.M.+	0.2	
6	2.1 +5S.M.+	0.1	
	3.3 +3S.M.+	0.1	
	Totals	100	100

Bibliography

Adamson, WA (1961)   *Lake and loch fishing for salmon & sea trout* London, Adam and Charles Black.

Allan, IRH and JA Ritter (1977)   Salmonid terminology *Journal du Conseil* 37 (3): 293-299

Allen, KR (1941)   Studies on the biology of the early stages of the salmon (*Salmo salar*) 1: Growth in the River Eden *Journal of Animal Ecology*: 9 (1): 1-23

— — (1944)   Studies on the biology of the early stages of the salmon (*Salmo salar*) 4. The smolt migration in the Thurso River in 1938 *Journal of Animal Ecology* 13 (1): 63-85

— — (1954)   Factors affecting the efficiency of restrictive regulations in fisheries management 1: Size limits *New Zealand Journal of Science and Technology* B 35: 498-529

— — (1969)   Limitations on production in salmonid populations in streams *in* TG Northcote (*ed*) *Symposium on salmon and trout in streams* HR MacMillan Lectures in Fisheries. University of British Columbia, Vancouver: 3-18

Alm, G (1950)   The sea trout population in the Ava stream *Report of the Institute of Freshwater Research, Drottningholm* 31: 26-56

Anon (1974)   Damage to salmon striking nylon nets *Trout and Salmon* 227: 38-40

Avondhu (1957)   Fishes of Lough Melvin *Salmon and Trout Magazine* 132: 153-156

Baranov, FI (1948)   *Theory and assessment of fishing* Moscow, Pishcrepromisdat

Barrett, JH and CM Yonge (1958)   *Pocket guide to the sea shore* London, Collins

Beams, Michael (1983)   *Peasants and Power. The Whiteboy movements and their control in pre-famine Ireland.* Sussex, The Harvester Press

Beamish, FWH (1980)   Biology of the North American anadromous sea lamprey *Petromyzon marinus. Canadian Journal of Fisheries and Aquatic Sciences* 37 (11): 1924-1943

Berg, LS (1962)   *Freshwater fishes of the USSR and adjacent countries*, Vol 1 Jerusalem, Israel program for scientific translations

Berry, J (1936)   British mammals and birds as enemies of the Atlantic salmon (*Salmo salar*)   *Avon Biological Research, Annual Report* 1934-35: 31-64

Bertmar, G (1979)   Home range, migrations and orientation mechanisms of the River Indalsalven trout *Salmo trutta* L. *Report of the Institute of Freshwater Research, Drottningholm* 58: 5-26

Bilton, HT (1973)   Effects of starvation and feeding on circulus formation on scales of younger sockeye salmon of four racial origins, and of one race of young kokanee, coho and chinook salmon *Proceedings of an international symposium on the ageing of fish*: 40-70; TB Bagenal (ed) Surrey, Gresham Press

Black Palmer (1882)   *Scotch loch fishing* Edinburgh, W Blackwood & Sons

Bohlin, T (1975)   A note on the aggressive behaviour of adult male sea trout to-wards "precocious" males during spawning *Report of the Institute of Freshwater Research, Drottningholm.* 54: 118

Brown, ME (1951)   The growth of brown trout (*Salmo trutta* L.) 4. The effect of food and temperature on the survival and growth of fry *Journal of experimental Biology* 28: 473-491

Burnet, AMR (1959)   Some observations on natural fluctuations of trout population numbers *New Zealand Journal of Science* 2: 410-421

Campbell, JS (1977)   Spawning characteristics of brown trout and sea trout (*Salmo trutta* L.) in Kirk Burn, River Tweed, Scotland *Journal of Fish Biology* 11: 217-229

Campbell, RN (1979)   Ferox trout, *Salmo trutta* L. and charr *Salvelinus alpinus* (L) in Scottish lochs *Journal of Fish Biology* 14: 1-9

Cane, A (1980)   The use of anglers' returns in the estimation of fishing success *Fisheries Management* 11 (4): 145-155

Chapman, DW (1958)   Studies on the life history of Alsea River steelhead *Journal of Wildlife Management* 22 (2): 123-134

Charlesworth, JK (1953)   *The geology of Ireland* Edinburgh, Oliver and Boyd

Chevenix Trench, C (1967)   *The poacher and the squire* London, Longman, Greene and Co. Ltd.

Child, AR, AM Burnell and NP Wilkins (1976)   The existence of two races of Atlantic salmon (*Salmo salar*) L. in the British Isles *Journal of Fish Biology* 8: 35-43

Chrystal, RA (1927)   *Angling theories and methods* London, Herbert Jenkins

— — (1939)   *Angling at Lochboisdale, South Uist. Notes on an angling journal 1882-1937* London, Witherby

Clapham, R (1950)   *Fishing for sea trout in tidal waters* Edinburgh, Oliver and Boyd

Couch, J (1869)   *A history of the fishes of the British Islands* London, Groombridge and Sons

Chrichton, MJ (1935)   Scale resorption in salmon and sea trout *Fisheries Scotland, Salmon Fisheries* 4: 1-8

Dahl, K (1910)   *Age and growth of salmon and trout in Norway* Kristiania, Central-trykkeriet: 115 pp

Davis, FM (1936)   An account of the fishing gear of England and Wales *Fisheries Investigation Series* Series II, 15 (2): 139 pp

Dawes, B (1947)   *The trematodes of British fishes* London, Ray Society

Day, F (1880-1884)   *The fishes of Great Britain and Ireland* London, Williams and Norgate

— — (1887)   *British and Irish Salmonidae* London, Williams and Norgate

Department of Agriculture and Technical Instruction (1902)   *Handbook of artificial flies for salmon and trout* Dublin, H.M.S.O.

Department responsible for Fisheries in Ireland. Annual Reports

Digby, JP (1951)   *Emigration — the answer* Dublin, Browne and Nolan

Dinneen, PS (1927)   *Foclóir Gaedhilge agus Béarla* Dublin, Educational Company of Ireland

Dixon, B (1931)   Age and growth of the sea trout (*Salmo trutta*) of the rivers Reda-and Dunajec *Journal du Conseil* 6 (3): 449-458

Dodge, DP and HR MacCrimmon (1970)   Vital statistics of a population of Great Lakes rainbow trout (*Salmo gairdneri*) characterised by an extended spawning season *Journal of the Fisheries Research Board of Canada* 27 (3): 613-618

Edgeworth, M (1969)   *Castle Rackrent* Oxford, Oxford University Press

Egglishaw, WJ and PE Shackley (1973)   An experiment on faster growth of salmon (*Salmo salar* (L)) in a Scottish stream *Journal of Fish Biology* 5: 197-204

— — and — — (1977)   Growth, survival and production of juvenile salmon and trout in a Scottish stream, 1966-'75 *Journal of Fish Biology* 11: 647-672

Elson, PF (1957)   The importance of size in the change from parr to smolt in Atlantic salmon. *Canadian Fish Culturist* 21: 1-6

— — (1957)   Number of salmon needed to maintain stocks *Canadian Fish Culturist* 21: 19-23

— — (1962)   Predator prey relationships between fish eating birds and Atlantic salmon *Bulletin of the Fisheries Research Board of Canada* 133: 87pp

Fahy, E (1977)   Characteristics of the freshwater occurrence of sea trout *Salmo trutta* in Ireland *Journal of Fish Biology* 11: 635-646

— — (1978)   Scale formation in sea trout smolts from two rivers with long estuaries *Foyle Fisheries Commission: Annual Report for 1978*

— — (1978)   Variation in some biological characteristics of British sea trout, *Salmo trutta* L. *Journal of Fish Biology* 13: 123-138

— — (1978)   Performance of a group of sea trout rod fisheries, Connemara, Ireland. *Fisheries Management* 9 (1): 22-31

— — (1979)   Performance of the Crumlin sea trout fishery, Co. Galway *Fishery Leaflet (Dublin)* 101: 12pp

— — (1979)   Sea trout from the tidal waters of the River Moy *Irish Fisheries Investigations* A 18: 11pp

— — (1979)   Prey selection by young trout fry (*Salmo trutta*) *Journal of Zoology, London* 190: 27-37

— — (1980)   'Growing season' as a factor in sea trout production *Journal of Fish Biology* 17: 541-546

— — (1980)   Sea trout from the Currane fishery in 1973 and 1974 *Irish Fisheries Investigations* A 19: 12pp

— — (1980)   *Eubothrium crassum* in migratory trout *Salmo trutta* L. in the sea *Journal of Fish Biology* 16: 99-104

— — (1981)   A review of the national sea trout catch *Fishery Leaflet (Dublin)* 113: 17 pp

— — (1981)   The Beltra fishery, Co Mayo, and its sea trout (*Salmo trutta*) stocks *Fisheries Bulletin (Dublin)* 4: 16 pp

— — (1981)   Sea trout and their fisheries from the Dublin fishery district *Fisheries Bulletin (Dublin)* 5: 10 pp

— — (1982)   Spawning trout *Salmo trutta* L populations in the Cummeragh system, Co. Kerry *Fisheries Bulletin (Dublin)* 5: 10 pp

— — (1982)   Why Currane stands alone *Trout and Salmon* 319: 47-48

— — (1982)   Tail of a trout *Trout and Salmon* 325: 61-62

— — (1982)   Fluctuations in the incidence of large trout in Ireland *Salmon and Trout Magazine* 224: 46-48

— — (1983)   Feeding ecology of feral rainbow trout *Salmo gairdneri* Richardson in Mulroy Bay, an Atlantic sea lough *Irish Naturalists' Journal* 21 (3): 103-107

— — (1983)   A niche for filling *Trout and Salmon* 332: 69-70

— — (1983)   Food and gut parasite burden of migratory trout *Salmo trutta* L. in the sea *Irish Naturalists' Journal* 22 (1): 11-18

— — (1983)   Have hatcheries a role in sea trout management? *Fishery Leaflet (Dublin)* 122: 12 pp

— — (1984)   Sea trout and their exploitation by draft net from the Feale and Munster Blackwater rivers in southern Ireland *Fisheries Bulletin (Dublin)* 8: 8 pp

— — (1985)   Protecting finnock as a sea trout conservation measure *Salmon and Trout Magazine* 230

— — and JJ Nixon (1982)   Spawning trout in Eastern Connemara *Fisheries Bulletin (Dublin)* 6: 11 pp

— —   and R Rudd (1983)   Characteristics of the riverine phase of large sea trout *Salmon and Trout Magazine* 225: 66-69

— — and — — (1984)   The use of weight-length relationships in sea trout stocks *Salmon and Trout Magazine* 228: 56-63

— — and WP Warren (1984)   Long lived sea trout, sea run *ferox? Salmon and Trout Magazine* 227: 72-75

Falkus, H (1977)   *Sea trout fishing. A guide to success* London, Witherby

Ferguson, A, K-J M Himberg and G Svardson (1978)   Systematics of the Irish pollan (*Coregonus pollan* Thompson): an electrophoretic comparison with other Holarctic Coregoninae *Journal of Fish Biology* 12: 221-233

— — and FM Mason (1981)   Allozyme evidence for reproductively isolated sympatric populations of brown trout *Salmo trutta* L., in Lough Melvin, Ireland *Journal of Fish Biology* 18: 629-642

Fleming, C (1982)   Population structure and biology of brown trout: a biochemical genetic approach *Fisheries Conference, 1982* Derry, The New University of Ulster

Frost, WE and ME Brown (1967)   *The trout* London, Collins, New Naturalist

Gee, AS, NJ Milner and RJ Hemsworth (1978)   The effect of density on mortality in juvenile Atlantic salmon (*Salmo salar*) *Journal of Animal Ecology* 47 (2): 497-505

Gibson, RJ (1978)   Recent changes in the population of juvenile Atlantic salmon in the Matamek River, Quebec, Canada *Journal du Conseil,* 38 (2): 201-207

Gloyne, RW (1973)   The 'growing season' at Eskdalemuir Observatory, Dumfriesshire *Meteorological Magazine* 102: 174-178

Greeley, JR (1933)   The growth rate of rainbow trout from some Michigan waters *Transactions of the American Fisheries Society* 63: 361-378

Gunther, ACLG (1880)   *An introduction to the study of fishes* Edinburgh, Adam and Charles Black

Hansen, LP (1980)   Net mark registrations on Atlantic salmon and sea trout in Norwegian rivers and coastal areas 1979 *International Council for the Exploration of the Sea* C.M. 1980 M: 33

Hardy, E (1951)   Birds versus salmon *Salmon and Trout Magazine* 132: 136-145.

Harris, GS (1970)   *Some aspects of the biology of Welsh sea trout* PhD. thesis, University of Liverpool

— — (1972)   Specimen sea trout from Welsh, English and Scottish waters *Salmon and Trout Magazine* 196: 15 pp

— — (1978)   *Salmon propagation in England and Wales* A report by the Association of river authorities/National Water Council working party: 62pp

Harris, JR (1952)   *The anglers' entomology* London, Collins, New Naturalist

Hartman, WL (1959)   Biology and vital statistics of rainbow trout in the Finger Lakes region, New York. *New York Fish and Game Journal* 6(2): 121-178

Hatch, RW (1957) Finger Lakes rainbows — spawning habits *New York State Conservationist* 11: 18-20

Hay, D (1975) Poaching and the game laws on Cannock Chase; from *Albion's fatal tree. Crime and society in 18th century England* London, Allen Lane.

Healy, TM (1913)   *Stolen waters: a page in the conquest of Ulster* London, Longmans, Green and Co.

Henzell, HP (1937)   *The art and craft of loch fishing* London, Philip Allan

— — (1949)   *Fishing for sea trout* London, Black

Holland, V (1957)   *Son of Oscar Wilde* Harmondsworth, Penguin Books

Holt, EWL (1907)   The artificial propagation of Salmonidae during the season of 1907-1908 *Report on the sea and inland fisheries of Ireland* Part II Scientific Investigations: 1-11

Jones, AN (1975)   A preliminary study of fish segregation in salmon spawning streams *Journal of Fish Biology* 7: 95-104

Jones, JW (1949)   Studies of the scales of young salmon *Salmo salar* L. in relation to growth, migration and spawning *Fishery Investigations, London* Series I, 5 (1): 1-23

Jensen, KW (1968)   Sea trout (*Salmo trutta* L.) of the River Istra, Western Norway, *Report of the Institute of Freshwater Research, Drottningholm* 32: 50-58

Kalleberg, H (1958)   Observations in a stream tank of territoriality and competition in juvenile salmon and trout *Report of the Institute of Freshwater Research, Drottningholm* 39: 55-98

Kendall, WC (1920)   What are rainbow trout and steelhead trout? *Transactions of the American Fisheries Society* 30: 187-199

King, EL and TA Edsall (1979)   Illustrated field guide for the classification of sea lamprey attack marks on the Great Lakes lake trout *Great Lakes Fishery Commission, special publication*

King, JW (1973)   Solar radiation changes and the weather *Nature, London* 243: 443-446

Kingsmill Moore, TC (1960)   *A man may fish* Bucks., Colin Smythe

Kislalloglu, M and RN Gibson (1977)   The feeding relationship of shallow water fishes in a Scottish sea loch *Journal of Fish Biology* 11: 257-266

Lamond, H (1916)   *The sea trout: a study in natural history* Manchester, Sherratt and Hughes

— — (1931)   *Loch Lomond* Glasgow, Jackson, Wylie and Co.

— — (1932)   *Days and ways of a Scottish angler* London, Philip Allan

Le Cren, ED (1973)   The population dynamics of young trout (*Salmo trutta*) in relation to density and territorial behaviour. *Conseil International pour l'exploration de la mer, Extrait des Rapports et Proces — verbaux* 164: 241-246

Lennon, RE (1954)   Feeding mechnaism of the sea lamprey and its effect on host fishes *Fishery Bulletin of the Fish and Wildlife Service* 56 (98): 247-293

Lesel, RY, Y Thérézien and R Vibert   Introduction de Salmonides aux Iles Kerguelen *Annales d'Hydrobiologie* 2 (2): 275-304

Lindroth, A (1956)   Distribution, territorial behaviour and movements of sea trout fry in the river Indalsalven *Report of the Institute of Freshwater Research, Drottningholm* 36: 104-119

— — (1962)   Baltic salmon fluctuations 2: Porpoises and salmon. *Report of the*

Institute of Freshwater Research, Drottningholm 44: 105-112

– – (1963)   The body/scale relationship in Atlantic salmon (*Salmo salar* L.). A preliminary report *Journal du Conseil* 28 (1): 137-152

Lockie, JD (1962)   Grey seals as competitors with man for salmon *In* Le Cren, ED and MW Holdgate (eds) *The exploitation of natural animal populations* Oxford, Blackwell Scientific Publications

Lynam, Shevawn (1975)   *Humanity Dick* London, Hamish Hamilton.

Madsen, FJ (1957)   On the food habits of some fish eating birds in Denmark *Danish Review of Game Biology* 3 (2): 19-83

Maitland, PS (1972)   *A key to the freshwater fishes of the British Isles* Freshwater Biological Association: Scientific publication 27: 139 pp

Mac Con Iomaire, S (1938)   *Cladaig Conamara* Dublin, Oifig an tSolathair.

MacCrimmon, HR (1971) World distribution of rainbow trout (*Salmo gairdneri*) *Journal of the Fisheries Research Board of Canada* 25 (5): 663-704

– – and JS Campbell (1969)   World distribution of brook trout, *Salvelinus fontinalis Journal of the Fisheries Research Board of Canada* 26 (7): 1699-1725

– – and TL Marshall (1968)   World distribution of brown trout, *Salmo trutta Journal of the Fisheries Research Board of Canada*, 25 (12): 2527-2548

M.A.F.F. (1981)   *Atlas of the Seas around the British Isles. Lowestoft.*

McNeill, J (1980)   A century of Irish summers *Irish Astronomical Journal* 14 (5/6): 165-176

Maxwell, WH (1832)   *Wild sports of the West* London, Gresham Publishing Co.

Menzies, WJM (1936)   *Sea trout and trout* London, Edward Arnold and Co.

Mills, DH (1965)   The distribution and food of the cormorant in Scottish inland waters *Freshwater and Salmon Fisheries Research* 35: 16 pp

– – (1967)   Predation on fish by other animals; from S.D. Gerking (ed) *The biological basis of freshwater fish production:* 377-397 Oxford, Blackwells Scientific Publications

– – (1971)   *Salmon and trout. A resource, its ecology, conservation and management* Edinburgh, Oliver and Boyd

Mottley, CM (1938)   Fluctuations in the intensity of the spawning runs of rainbow trout at Paul Lake *Journal of the Fisheries Research Board of Canada* 4 (2): 69-87

Munro, WR and KH Balmain (1956)   Observations on the spawning runs of brown trout in the South Queich, Loch Leven *Freshwater and Salmon Fisheries Research* 13: 17 pp

Murphy, GJ and L Shapovalov (1951)   A preliminary analysis of northern California salmon and steelhead runs. *California Fish and Game* 37: 497-507

Nall, GH (1930)   *The life of the sea trout; especially in Scottish waters* London, Seeley Service

– – (1930)   Sea trout from the River Tweed. *Fisheries, Scotland, Salmon Fisheries* 5: 59 pp

– – (1931)   Irish sea trout.*Proceedings of the Royal Irish Academy* 40 B (1): 1-36

– – (1931)   Sea trout from the Solway rivers: *Fisheries, Scotland, Salmon Fisheries* 3: 72 pp

– – (1933)   The sea trout of the Dovey *Salmon and Trout Magazine* 71: 169-186.

– – and WJM Menzies (1931)   Difficulties of age determination and length calculations from the scales of sea trout (*Salmo trutta*) *Fisheries, Scotland, Salmon Fisheries* 5: 12 pp

Nelson, JB (1978) *The Sulidae* Oxford, Oxford University Press

Norman, JR and PH Greenwood (1963) *A History of Fishes* London, Ernest Benn

Northcote, TG (1962) Migratory behaviour of juvenile rainbow trout *Salmo gairdneri*, in outlet and inlet streams of Loon lake, British Columbia *Journal of the Fishery Research Board of Canada.* 19 (2): 201-270

O'Connor, R and BJ Whelan (1973) *An economic evaluation of Irish salmon fishing I: The visiting anglers.* Economic and Social Research Institute (Dublin) 68: 66 pp

— — — — and A McCashin (1974) *An economic evaluation of Irish salmon fishing II: The Irish anglers.* Economic and Social Research Institute (Dublin) 75: 96 pp

O'Donoghue, CH and EM Boyd (1931) A preliminary investigation of the food of the sea trout (*Salmo trutta*) *Fisheries, Scotland, Salmon Fisheries* 3: 15 pp

— — and — — (1932) A second investigation of the food of the sea trout (*Salmo trutta*) *Fisheries, Scotland, Salmon Fisheries* 2: 18 pp

— — and — — (1934) A third investigation of the food of the sea trout (*Salmo trutta*) with a note in the food of the perch (*Perca fluviatilis*) *Fisheries, Scotland, Salmon Fisheries* 2: 21 pp

Orcutt, DB, BR Pulliam and A Arp (1968) Characteristics of steelhead trout redds in Idaho streams *Transactions of the American Fisheries Society* 97: 42-45

Ottaway, EM, PA Carling, A Clarke and NA Reader (1981) Observations on the structure of brown trout *Salmo trutta* L. redds *Journal of Fish Biology* 19: 593-607

O'Tuathaigh, G (1972) *Ireland before the Famine 1798-1848* Dublin, Gill and Macmillan.

Pautz, CF and RC Meigs (1940) Studies on the life history of the Puget Sound steelhead trout (*Salmo gairdneri*) *Transactions of the American Fisheries Society* 70: 209-220

Payne, RH, AR Child and A Forrest (1971) Geographical variation in the Atlantic salmon *Nature, London* 231: 250-252

Payne, RH, AR Child and A Forrest (1972) The existence of natural hybrids between the European trout and the Atlantic salmon *Journal of Fish Biology* 4: 233-236

Pemberton, R (1976) Sea trout in north Argyll sea lochs, population, distribution and movements *Journal of Fish Biology* 9: 157-179

— — (1976) Sea trout in north Argyll sea lochs, II diet *Journal of Fish Biology* 9: 195-208

Peterson, CGJ (1918) The sea bottom and its production of fish food. *Report of the Danish Biological Station* 21: 1-44

Piggins, DJ (1959) Investigations on predators of salmon smolts and parr *Annual Report and Statement of accounts, Salmon Research Trust of Ireland* Appendix No 1: 12 pp

— — (1968) An anlysis of recapture data from tagged sea trout kelts 1960/1966. *Annual report and Statement of accounts, Salmon Research Trust of Ireland* Appendix No 2: 38-48

Pratten, DJ & WM Shearer (1983) Sea trout of the North Esk *Fisheries Management* 14 (2): 49-65

— — and — — (1983) The migration of North Esk sea trout *Fisheries Management* 14 (3): 99-113

Purdom, CE (1979) Fish farming in the UK *Biologist* 26 (4): 153-161

Rae, BB (1965) The food of the common porpoise *Journal of Zoology* 146: 114-122

— — (1968)　The food of seals in Scottish waters *Department of Agriculture and Fisheries for Scotland; Marine Research* 2: 23 pp

— — (1973)　Further observations on the food of seals *Journal of Zoology, London* 169: 287-297

Republican Publications (1970)　*Stolen Waters: the case for public ownership of Ireland's rivers and lakes.* 4th edition, Dublin

Rooney, P (1966)　*Captain Boycott* Tralee, Anvil Books

Ryman, N (ed) (1981)　Fish gene pools *Ecological Bulletin* 34: 112 pp

— — and G Stahl (1980)　Genetic changes in hatchery stocks of brown trout (*Salmo trutta*) *Canadian Journal of Fisheries and Aquatic Science* 37: 82-87

Salmon Research Trust of Ireland Inc. Annual Reports

Savvaitova, KA (1980)　Taxonomy and biogeography of charrs in the Palearctic, *in* Balon EK (ed) *Charrs, salmonid fishes of the genus Salvelinus* The Hague, W Junk

Schwiebert, E (1979)　*Trout* London, Andre Deutsch

Scott, J (1960)　*Salmon and trout fishing up to date* London, Seeley Service

Seeley, HG (1886)　*The fresh-water fishes of Europe* London, Cassell

Shapovalov, L and AC Taft (1954)　The life histories of steelhead rainbow trout (*Salmo gairdneri*) and silver salmon (*Oncorhynchus kisutch*) with special reference to Waddell Creek, California, and recommendations regarding their management *Californian Department of Fisheries and Game, Fisheries Bulletin* 98: 375 pp

Simkiss, K (1973)　Calcium metabolism of fish in relation to ageing *Proceedings of an international symposium on the ageing of fish*: 1-12 ed. TB Bagenal. Surrey, Gresham Press.

Smith, SB (1960)　A note on two stocks of steelhead trout (*Salmo gairdneri*) in Capilano River, British Columbia *Journal of the Fisheries Research Board of Canada* 17 (5): 739-742

Southern, R (1934)　The salmon industry: a statistical survey of the industry *Irish Trade Journal*: 105-110

Spencer, S (1968)　*Salmon and sea trout in wild places* London, Witherby

— — (1969)　*Newly from the sea* London, Witherby

Stauffer, TM (1972)　Age, growth and downstream migration of juvenile rainbow trout in a lake Michigan tributary *Transactions of the American Fisheries Society* 101: 18-28

Steven, DM (1948)　Studies on animal caroteniods. I Carotenoids of the brown trout (*Salmo trutta* L) *Journal of experimental Biology* 25: 369-387

— — (1949)　Studies on animal carotenoids. II Carotenoids in the reproductive cycle of brown trout. *Journal of experimental Biology* 26: 295-303

Stuart, H (1952)　*The book of the sea trout, with some chapters on salmon* Rafael Sabitini (ed). First published 1917, London, Jonathan Cape

Sutterlin, AM, P Harmon and H Barchard (1976)　The culture of brook trout in salt water. *Technical report 636. Environment Canada, Fisheries and Marine Service*: 17 pp

Svärdson, G (1955) Salmon stock fluctuations in the Baltic Sea. *Report of the Institute of Freshwater Research, Drottningholm* 36: 226-262

— — and Å Fagerstrom (1982)　Adaptive differences in the long distance migration of some trout (*Salmo trutta* L) stocks *Report of the Institute of Freshwater Research, Drottningholm* 60: 51-80

Swain, A and WG Hartley (1959)　Movements of sea trout off the east coast of England *Annual Report of the Challenger Society*

Swift, DR (1961)   The annual growth rate cycle in brown trout (*Salmo trutta* L) and its cause. *Journal of experimental Biology* 38: 595-604

Sych, R (1967)   Age determination of sea trout (*Salmo trutta* L) during formation of annual rings *Rocznik nauk rolniczych* (H) 90 (2): 305-325

— — (1967)   Confidence estimation of a fish age determination from scales as exemplified by sea trout (*Salmo trutta* L) *Rocznik nauk rolniczych* (H) 90 (2): 281-303

— — (1967)   Interpretation of the scales of Vistula sea trout (*Salmo trutta* L) *Acta Hydrobiologia* 9 (3-4): 231-280

— — (1971)   Some considerations on the theory of age determination of fish from their scales — finding proofs of reliability *EIFAC Technical paper* 13: 68 pp. Rome, F.A.O.

Tchernavin, V (1939)   The origin of salmon, its ancestry marine or freshwater? *Salmon and Trout Magazine* 95: 120-140

Thackeray, WM (1902)   *The Paris sketch book of Mr MA Titmarsh and the Irish sketch book* London, Macmillan and Co.

Thompson, W (1856)   *The natural history of Ireland* Vol IV London, Bohn

Tuchman, BW (1978)   *A distant mirror, the calamitous 14th century.* Harmondsworth, Penguin Books

Twomey, E (1956)   Salmon of the river Moy *Department of Lands: Report on the Sea and Inland Fisheries for 1956*: 12 pp

Van Oosten J (1957)   Chapter V. Skin and Scales in *The physiology of fishes* Vol 1, ME Brown (ed). New York, Academic Press

Van Velson, RC (1974)   Self sustaining rainbow trout (*Salmo gairdneri*) population in McConaughy Reservoir, Nebraska *Transactions of the American Fisheries Society* 103 (1): 59-64

Varley, ME (1967)   *British freshwater fishes: factors affecting their distribution* London, Fishing News (Books)

Vaughan, WE *in* FSL Lyons and RAJ Hawkins (1980)   *Ireland under the Union. Essays in honour of TW Moody.* Oxford, Clarendon Press

Vibert, R (1950)   Recherches sur la Salmon de l'Adour (*Salmo salar* L.), ages, croissance, cycle genetique, races *Annales de la Station Centrale d'Hydrobiologie Appliquee* 3: 35-249

Waind, KD (1971)   Investigations on the Irish Sea sand eel fishery 1971 *Irish Sea Fisheries Board:* 20 pp

Walton, Izaak (1962)   *The compleat angler* London, Everyman's Library

Went, AEJ (1938)   The salmon fishery. A statistical survey of the industry *Irish Trade Journal* 13: 8-13; 79-86

— — (1956)   The Irish drift net fishery for salmon *Journal of the Department of Agriculture, Dublin* 52: 131-145

— — (1957)   Notes on the Irish salmon industry (1924-1955) *Journal of the Department of Agriculture* 53: 70-89

— — (1962)   Irish sea trout, a review of investigations to date *Scientific Proceedings of the Royal Dublin Society* 1 (10): 265-296

— — (1964)   Pepper's ghost, alas a ghost no more! *Salmon and Trout Magazine* 175: 22-24

— — (1964)   The pursuit of salmon in Ireland *Proceedings of the Royal Irish Academy* 63 B (6): 191-244

— — (1967)   Review of the Irish salmon industry *Irish Fisheries Investigations* A 1: 1-25

— — (1968)   'Specimen' brown trout and sea trout from Irish waters *Irish Fisheries Investigations* A 3: 15 pp

West, B, D Cabot and M Greer-Walker (1975)   The food of the cormorant *Phalacrocorax carbo* at some breeding colonies in Ireland *Proceedings of the Royal Irish Academy* 75 B (14): 285-304

Whelan, BJ, R O'Connor and A McCashin (1974)   *An economic evaluation of Irish salmon fishing: III The commercial fishermen* Economic and Social Research Institute (Dublin) 78: 100 pp

White, HC (1940)   Life history of sea running brook trout (*Salvelinus fontinalis*) of Moser River, N.S. *Journal of the Fisheries Research Board of Canada* 5: 176-186

— — (1941)   Migratihg behaviour of sea running *Salvelinus fontinalis*. *Journal of the Fisheries Research Board of Canada* 5: 258-264

— — (1942)   Sea life of the brook trout (*Salvelinus fontinalis*) *Journal of the Fisheries Research Board of Canada* 5: 471-473

Wilder, DG (1952)   A comparative study of anadromous and freshwater populations of brook trout (*Salvelinus fontinalis* (Mitchill)) *Journal of the Fisheries Research Board of Canada* 9 (4): 169-203

Williams, C (1961)   *A dictionary of trout flies* London, Adam and Charles Black

Withler, IL (1966)   Variability in life history characteristics of steelhead trout (*Salmo gairdneri*) along the Pacific coast of North America *Journal of the Fishery Research Board of Canada* 23 (3): 365-392

Woodham-Smith, C (1962)   *The Great Hunger, Ireland 1845-9* London, Hamish Hamilton

Worthington, EB (1940 and 1941)   Rainbows: a report on attempts to acclimatize rainbow trout in Britain *Salmon and Trout Magazine* 100: 241-261; 101: 62-98

Wyatt, T (1976)   Food chains in the sea, Chap. 14 in *The ecology of the seas* DH Cushing and JJ Walsh (eds): 341-358. London, Blackwell Scientific Publications

Yarrell, W (1854)   *A history of British fishes* Vol 1. London, John van Voorst

Yevsin, VN (1977)   Morphological characteristics and variability of the summer sea trout (*Salmo trutta*) from the Pulong'a and Malaya Kumzhevaya Rivers *Journal of Ichthyology* 17 (3): 350-356

Index